THE *Lyric*

CW00832979

Show Songs

Complete Lyrics for 267 Songs
From 100 Musicals

 HLE

HAL LEONARD EUROPE

Distributed by Music Sales

Exclusive Distributors:
Music Sales Limited
8/9 Frith Street, London W1D 3JB, England.
Music Sales Pty Limited
120 Rothschild Avenue, Rosebery, NSW 2018, Australia.

Order No. HLE90001989
ISBN 1-84449-190-0
This book © Copyright 2004 by Hal Leonard Europe

Printed in the Great Britain.

Your Guarantee of Quality
As publishers, we strive to produce every book to the highest
commercial standards.
Throughout, the printing and binding have been planned to ensure a sturdy,
attractive publication which should give years of enjoyment.
If your copy fails to meet our high standards, please inform us and we will gladly
replace it.

www.musicsales.com

Preface

If the stage musical's golden age was the 1950s, it has made the journey into the 21st century in some considerable style. The melodies may still be the initial attraction for audiences but it is the lyrics that have always added something special to the best musical numbers. Freed from demands of standalone pop songs, the lyrics of the best show songs – which of course must also advance a plot – continue to be among the most literate, witty and inventive ever written.

The great stage lyricists of the 20th century took the 19th century example of W.S. Gilbert forward into contemporary productions that at their best perfectly caught the flavour and the speech patterns of the times. Ira Gershwin and Lorenz Hart wrote matchless lyrics: funny, wry, inventive and sophisticated while still being highly accessible to popular audiences. Oscar Hammerstein found the perfect words for Richard Rodgers' lush melodies, while Cole Porter, Alan Jay Lerner and Frank Loesser established high standards that would inspire Fred Ebb, Stephen Sondheim, Tim Rice, Don Black and a whole new generation of lyricists with a broadening range of themes.

That musicals were often seen as a US genre was to some extent a reflection of the achievement of those pioneering lyricists for whom American vernacular speech seemed to offer exactly the right rhythms and cadences for musical drama.

Later Britain, whose strait-laced Edwardian operettas had provided the initial spark for the Broadway musical, would find a voice of its own and make a significant contribution to the genre with such diverse shows as *Stop The World I Want To Get Off!*, *Pickwick*, *The Phantom Of The Opera* and even that quintessential Hollywood tragedy *Sunset Boulevard*.

The best musical songs always seem to take on a life of their own so that many people familiar with them from the radio are surprised when they finally encounter them in context, in a show or a film of a show, seamlessly fitting into the action. It is the musical equivalent of the man who finally went to see a Shakespeare play and was puzzled to find that it was full of quotations.

He should not have been surprised, and neither should we when we see, laid out in this book, so many superbly written songs, all taken from musicals. Some have outstripped the fame of the shows in which they originally appeared. Others are forever destined to evoke the first time we saw this or that classic production. In all cases, even those where the melodies are particularly cherished, it is the lyrics that seem to account for at least half of the song's enduring popularity.

Contents

Lyrics

Adelaide's Lament

Words & Music by Frank Loesser

from *Guys & Dolls*

The av'rage unmarried female,
Basically insecure,
Due to some long frustration may react
With psychosomatic symptoms
Difficult to endure,
Affecting the upper respiratory tract.

In other words,
Just from waiting around
For that plain little band of gold,
A person can develop a cold.
You can spray her wherever you figure
The streptococci lurk,
You can give her a shot for whatever
    she's got,
But it just won't work.
If she's tired of getting the fish-eye
From the hotel clerk,
A person can develop a cold.

Spoken:
It says here,

Sung:
The female remaining single,
Just in the legal sense,
Shows a neurotic tendency. See note.

Spoken:
Note:

Sung:
Chronic, organic syndromes,
Toxic or hypertense,
Involving the eye, the ear, and the nose,
    and throat.
In other words,
Just from worrying whether the wedding is on
    or off,
A person can develop a cough.
You can feed her all day
With the Vitamin A and the Bromo Fizz,
But the medicine never gets anywhere near
Where the trouble is.
If she's getting a kind of a name for herself,
And the name ain't "his,"
A person can develop a cough.

And furthermore, just from stalling and stalling,
And stalling the wedding trip,
A person can develop La grippe.
When they get on the train for Niag'ra,
And she can hear church bells chime,
The compartment is air conditioned,
And the mood sublime.
Then they get off at Saratoga
For the fourteenth time,
A person can develop La grippe,
(Hm!) La grippe,
La post nasal drip,
With the wheezes and the sneezes
And a sinus that's really a pip!
From a lack of community property
And a feeling she's getting too old,
A person can develop a bad, bad cold.

Ain't Misbehavin'

Words by Andy Razaf
Music by Thomas "Fats" Waller & Harry Brooks

from *Ain't Misbehavin'*

Verse:
Boy:
Tho's it's a fickle age
With flirting all the rage,
Here is one bird with self-control;
Happy inside my cage.
I know who I love best,
Thumbs down for all the rest,
My love was given, heart and soul,
So it can withstand the test.

Refrain:
No one to talk with,
All by myself.
No one to walk with,
But I'm happy on the shelf.
Ain't misbehavin',
I'm savin' my love for you.

I know for certain,
The one I love.
I'm through with flirtin',
It's just you I'm thinkin' of.
Ain't misbehavin',
I'm savin' my love for you.

Like Jack Horner,
In the corner,
Don't go nowhere.
What do I care?
Your kisses are worth waitin' for;
Believe me.

I don't stay out late,
Don't care to go.
I'm home about eight,
Just me and my radio.
Ain't misbehavin',
I'm saving my love for you.

Verse:
Girl:
Your type of man is rare,
I know you really care.
That's why my conscience never sleeps,
When you're away somewhere.
Sure was a lucky day,
When fate sent you my way,
And made you mine alone for keeps,
Ditto to all you say.

Repeat Refrain

All At Once You Love Her

Words by Oscar Hammerstein II
Music by Richard Rodgers

from *Pipe Dream*

You start to light
Her cigarette,
And all at once
You love her.
You've scarcely talked,
You've scarcely met,
But all at once
You love her.

You like her eyes,
You tell her so.
She thinks you're wise
And clever.
You kiss goodnight
And then you know
You'll kiss goodnight
Forever!
You wonder where your heart can go
And all at once you know.

All Good Gifts

Words & Music by Stephen Schwartz

from *Godspell*

We plow the fields and scatter
The good seed on the land,
But it is fed and watered
By God's almighty hand.

He sends the snow in winter,
The warmth to swell the grain,
The breezes and the sunshine,
And soft refreshing rain.

Refrain:
All good gifts around us
Are sent from heaven above.
Then thank the Lord,
O thank the Lord for all His love.

We thank Thee, then O Father,
For all things bright and good,
The seed time and the harvest,
Our life, our health, our food.

No gifts have we to offer,
For all Thy love imparts,
But that which Thou desirest,
Our humble, thankful hearts.

Refrain

I really want to thank You, Lord,
I want to thank You, Lord,
Thank You for all of Your love,
I want to thank You, Lord,
I want to thank You for love.
Oh, thank You, Lord!

All I Ask Of You

Music by Andrew Lloyd Webber
Lyrics by Charles Hart
Additional Lyrics by Richard Stilgoe

from *The Phantom Of The Opera*

Raoul:
No more talk of darkness,
Forget these wide-eyed fears:
I'm here, nothing can harm you,
My words will warm and calm you.
Let me be your freedom,
Let daylight dry your tears:
I'm here, with you, beside you,
To guard you and to guide you.

Christine:
Say you love me every waking moment,
Turn my head with talk of summertime.
Say you need me with you now and always;
Promise me that all you say is true;
That's all I ask of you.

Raoul:
Let me be your shelter;
Let me be your light.
You're safe,
No one will find you;
Your fears are far behind you.

Christine:
All I want is freedom,
A world with no more night;
And you, always beside me,
To hold me and to hide me.

Raoul:
Then say you'll share with me one love, one
    lifetime;
Let me lead you from your solitude.
Say you need me with you
Here beside you.
Anywhere you go, let me go too.
Christine, that's all I ask of you.

Christine:
Say you'll share with me one love, one lifetime,
Say the word and I will follow you.

Together:
Share each day with me, each night, each
    morning.

Christine:
Say you love me!

Raoul:
You know I do.

Together:
Love me, that's all I ask of you.
Anywhere you go, let me go too.
Love me, that's all I ask of you.

Alone At The Drive-In Movie

Words & Music by Warren Casey & Jim Jacobs

from *Grease*

I'm all alone,
At the drive-in movie,
It's a feeling
That ain't too groovy,
Watching werewolves without you.

Gee, it's no fun
Drinking beer in the back seat,
All alone
Just ain't too neat,
At the passion pit, wanting you.

And when the intermission elf
Moves the clock's hands,
While he's eating ev'rything
Sold at the stand.

When there's one minute to go,
'Til the lights go down low,
I'll be holding the speaker knobs,
Missing you so.

Can't believe it,
Unsteamed windows I can see through,
Might as well be in an igloo,
'Cause the heater doesn't work
As good as you.
(Baby, come back.)

Always True To You In My Fashion

Words & Music by Cole Porter

from *Kiss Me, Kate*

Oh, Bill,
Why can't you behave?
Oh, why can't you behave?
How in hell can you be jealous,
When you know, baby, I'm your slave?
I'm just mad for you,
And I'll always be,
But naturally,

If a custom tailored vet
Asks me out for something wet,
When the vet begins to pet,
I cry, "Hooray!"
But I'm always true to you, darlin',
   in my fashion,
Yes, I'm always true to you, darlin',
   in my way.

I enjoy a tender pass
By the boss of Boston, Mass.
Through his pass is middle class,
And not "Back Bay!"
But I'm always true to you, darlin',
   in my fashion,
Yes, I'm always true to you, darlin',
   in my way.

There's a madman known as "Mack"
Who is planning to attack.
If his mad attack means a Cadillac,
Okay!

But I'm always true to you, darlin',
   in my fashion,
Yes, I'm always true to you, darlin',
   in my way.

I've been asked to have a meal
By a big tycoon in steel.
If the meal includes a deal,
Accept I may!
But I'm always true to you, darlin',
   in my fashion,
Yes, I'm always true to you, darlin',
   in my way.

I could never curl my lip
To a dazzlin' diamond clip,
Though the clip meant "let 'er rip,"
I'd not say "Nay!"
But I'm always true to you, darlin',
   in my fashion,
Yes, I'm always true to you, darlin',
   in my way.

There's an oil man known as "Tex"
Who is keen to give me checks,
And his checks I fear,
Mean that Tex is here to stay!
But I'm always true to you, darlin',
   in my fashion,
Yes, I'm always true to you, darlin',
   in my way.

The American Dream

Music by Claude-Michel Schönberg
Lyrics by Alain Boublil & Richard Maltby Jr.

from *Miss Saigon*

I'm fed up with small time hustles,
I'm too good to waste my talent for greed.
I need room to flex my muscles
In an ocean where the big sharks feed.
Make me Yankee, they're my family.
They're selling what people need.

What's that I smell in the air,
The American dream.
Sweet as a new millionaire,
The American dream.
Pre-packed and ready to wear,
The American dream.
Fat, like a choc'late éclair
When you suck out the cream.
Luck by the tail, how can you fail?
And best of all, it's for sale,
The American dream.

Greasy drinks make life so sleazy.
In the States I'll build a club that's four-starred.
Men like me there have things easy,
They have a lawyer and a body-guard.
To the johns there I'll sell blondes there,
That they can charge on a card.

What's that I smell in the air?
The American dream.
Sweet as a suite in Belair,
The American dream.
Girls can buy tits by the pair,
The American dream.
Bald people think they'll grow hair,
The American dream.
Call-girls are lining Times Square,
The American dream.
Bums have money to spare,
The American dream.
Cars that have bars take you there,
The American dream.
On stage each night Fred Astaire,
The American dream.

Pop the champagne,
It's time we all entertain
My American dream.

Bus-boys can buy the hotel,
The American dream.
Wall street is ready to sell,
The American dream.
Come make a life from thin air,
The American dream.
Come and get more than your share,
The American dream.
There I will crown Miss China-town.
All yours for ten percent down,
The American dream.

And All That Jazz

Words by Fred Ebb
Music by John Kander

from *Chicago*

Come on, babe, why don't we paint the town,
And all that jazz!
I'm gonna rouge my knees and roll my
   stockings down,
And all that jazz!
Start the car, I know a whoopee spot,
Where the gin is cold but the piano's hot.
It's just a noisy hall where there's a nightly
   brawl,
And all that jazz!

Slick your hair and wear your buckle shoes,
And all that jazz!
I hear that Father Dip is gonna blow the blues,
And all that jazz!
Hold on, hon', we're gonna bunny hug,
I bought some aspirin down at United Drug,
In case we shake apart and want a brand new
   start
To do that jazz!

Oh, I'm gonna see my Sheba shimmy shake.
(And all that jazz!)
Oh, she's gonna shimmy till her garters break.
(And all that jazz!)
Show her where to park her girdle,
Oh, her mother's blood'd curdle
If she'd hear her baby's queer
For all that jazz!

Voice 1:
Find a flask, we're playing fast and loose,
And all that jazz!
Right up here is where I store the juice,
And all that jazz!
Come on babe, we're gonna brush the sky.
I betcha Lucky Lindy never flew so high,
'Cause in the stratosphere, how could he lend
   an ear
To all that jazz!

Voice 2:
Oh, you're gonna see your Sheba shimmy
   shake,
And all that jazz!
Oh, I'm gonna shimmy till my garters break,
And all that jazz!
Show me where to park my girdle,
Oh, my mother's blood'd curdle,
If she'd hear her baby's queer
For all that jazz!

No, I'm no-one's wife,
But, oh, I love my life,
And all that jazz!
(Spoken) That jazz!

Anthem

Words & Music by Benny Andersson, Tim Rice & Bjorn Ulvaeus

from *Chess*

No man, no madness,
Though their sad power may prevail,
Can possess, conquer my country's heart,
They rise to fail.

She is eternal;
Long before nations' lines were drawn
When no flags flew, when no armies stood,
My land was born.

And you ask me why I love her
Through wars, death and despair.
She is the constant,
We who don't care.
And you wonder,
Will I leave her but how?
I cross over borders
But I'm still there now.

How can I leave her?
Where would I start?
Let man's petty nations
Tear themselves apart.

My land's only borders
Lie around my heart.

Another Hundred People

Words & Music by Stephen Sondheim

from *Company*

Another hundred people just got off the train
And came up through the ground,
While another hundred people just got off the
  bus
And are looking around
At another hundred people who got off of the
  plane
And are looking at us,
Who got off of the train
And the plane and the bus,
Maybe yesterday.

It's a city of strangers.
Some come to work, some to play.
A city of strangers,
Some come to stare, some to stay.
And ev'ry day,
The ones who stay,

Can find each other in the crowded streets
And the guarded parks,
By the rusty fountains and the dusty trees
With the battered barks,
And they walk together past the postered walls
With the crude remarks.

And they meet at parties through the friends of
  friends
Who they never know.
Will you pick me up or do I meet you there,
Or shall we let it go?

Did you get my message 'cause I looked in
  vain?
Can we see each other Tuesday if it doesn't
  rain?
Look, I'll call you in the morning or my service
  will explain.
And another hundred people just got off the
  train.

Another Op'nin', Another Show

Words & Music by Cole Porter

from *Kiss Me, Kate*

Another op'nin', another show,
In Philly, Boston, or Baltimo'e.
A chance for stage folks to say, "hello,"
Another op'nin' of another show.

Another job that you hope, at last,
Will make your future forget your past.
Another pain, where the ulcers grow,
Another op'nin' of another show!

Four weeks you rehearse and rehearse.
Three weeks and it couldn't be worse.
One week, will it ever be right?
Then out of the hat it's that big first night!

The overture is about to start.
You cross your fingers and hold your heart.
It's curtain time and away we go.
Another op'nin' of another show.

Another Suitcase In Another Hall

Music by Andrew Lloyd Webber
Lyrics by Tim Rice

from *Evita*

Verse 1:
I don't expect my love affairs to last for long;
Never fool myself that my dreams will come
   true.
Being used to trouble I anticipate it,
But all the same I hate it,
Wouldn't you?

Refrain:
So what happens now?

Choir:
Another suitcase in another hall

So what happens now?

Choir:
Take your picture off another wall

Where am I going to?

Choir:
You'll get by, you always have before

Where am I going to?

Verse 2:
Time and time again I've said that I don't care;
That I'm immune to gloom, that I'm hard
   through and through:
But every time it matters all my words desert
   me;
So anyone can hurt me- and they do.

Refrain

Verse 3:
Call in three months' time and I'll be fine I
   know;
Well maybe not that fine, but I'll survive
   anyhow:
I won't recall the names and places of this sad
   occasion;
But that's no consolation, here and now.

Refrain

Choir:
Don't ask any more.

Any Dream Will Do

Music by Andrew Lloyd Webber
Lyrics by Tim Rice

from *Joseph And The Amazing Technicolor® Dreamcoat*

I closed my eyes,
Drew back the curtain,
To see for certain
What I thought I knew.
Far, far away,
Someone was weeping,
But the world was sleeping.
Any dream will do.

I wore my coat,
With golden lining,
Bright colours shining,
Wonderful and new.
And in the east,
The dawn was breaking,
And the world was waking.
Any dream will do.

A crash of drums,
A flash of light,
My golden coat
Flew out of sight.
The colours faded into darkness,
I was left alone.

May I return,
To the beginning?
The light is dimming,
And the dream is too.
The world and I,
We are still waiting,
Still hesitating.
Any dream will do.

As If We Never Said Goodbye

Music by Andrew Lloyd Webber
Lyrics by Don Black & Christopher Hampton
With contributions by Amy Powers

from *Sunset Boulevard*

I don't know why I'm frightened,
I know my way around here.
The cardboard trees, the painted seas,
   the sound here.
Yes, a world to rediscover,
But I'm not in any hurry,
And I need a moment.

The whispered conversations in
   overcrowded hallways,
The atmosphere as thrilling here
As always.
Feel the early morning madness,
Feel the magic in the making.
Why, everything's as if we never
   said goodbye.

I've spent so many mornings,
Just trying to resist you.
I'm trembling now, you can't know how
   I've missed you,
Missed the fairytale adventures
In this ever-spinning playground.
We were young together.

I'm coming out of makeup,
The light's already burning.
Not long until the cameras will
   start turning,
And the early morning madness,
And the magic in the making,
Yes, everything's as if we never
   said goodbye.

I don't want to be alone,
That's all in the past.
This world's waited long enough,
I've come home at last.

And this time will be bigger,
And brighter than we knew it.
So watch me fly, we all know I can do it.
Could I stop my hand from shaking?
Has there ever been a moment
With so much to live for?

The whispered conversations in
   overcrowded hallways,
So much to say, not just today, but always.
We'll have early morning madness,
We'll have magic in the making.
Yes, everything's as if we never said goodbye,
Yes, everything's as if we never said goodbye.
We taught the world new ways to dream.

As Long As He Needs Me

Words & Music by Lionel Bart

from *Oliver!*

As long as he needs me,
Oh yes, he does need me,
In spite of what you see
I'm sure that he needs me.

Who else would love him still
When they've been used so ill?
He knows I always will,
As long as he needs me.

I miss him so much
When he is gone,
But when he's near me
I don't let on.

The way I feel inside,
The love I have to hide.
The hell! I've got my pride
As long as he needs me.

He doesn't say the things he should.
He acts the way he thinks he should.
But all the same I'll play
This game his way.

As long as he needs me,
I know where I must be,
I'll cling on steadfastly,
As long as he needs me.

As long as life is long
I'll love him right or wrong,
And somehow I'll be strong,
As long as he needs me.

If you are lonely
Then you will know,
When someone needs you
You love them so.

I won't betray his trust
Though people say I must,
I've got to stay true
Just as long as he needs me.

At The End Of The Day

Music by Claude-Michel Schönberg
Original Lyrics by Alain Boublil & Jean-Marc Natel
English Lyrics by Herbert Kretzmer

from *Les Misérables*

At the end of the day you're another day older.
And that's all you can say for the life of the
  poor.
It's a struggle, it's a war.
And there's nothing that anyone's giving.
One more day standing about,
What is it for?
One less day to be living.

At the end of the day you're another day colder.
And the shirt on your back doesn't keep out the
  chill.
And the righteous hurry past,
They don't hear the little ones crying.
And the winter is coming on fast, ready to kill.
One day nearer to dying.

At the end of the day there's another day
  dawning.
And the sun in the morning is waiting to rise.
Like the waves crash on the sand,
Like a storm that'll break any second,
There's a hunger in the land.
There's a reckoning still to be reckoned.
And there's gonna be hell to pay
At the end of the day.

At the end of the day you get nothing for
  nothing.
Sitting flat on your butt doesn't buy any bread.
There are children back at home.
And the children have got to be fed.
And you're lucky to be in a job, and in a bed.
And we're counting our blessings.

At the end of the day, it's another day over,
With enough in your pocket to last for a week.
Pay the landlord, pay the shop.
Keep on grafting as long as you're able.
Keep on grafting till you drop,
Or it's back to the crumbs off the table.
Well, you've got to pay your way,
At the end of the day.

Bali Ha'i

Lyrics by Oscar Hammerstein II
Music by Richard Rodgers

from *South Pacific*

Most people live on a lonely island,
Lost in the middle of a foggy sea.
Most people long for another island,
One where they know they would like to be.

Bali Ha'i
May call you,
Any night,
Any day.
In your heart
You'll hear it call you:
"Come away,
Come away."

Bali Ha'i
Will whisper
On the wind
Of the sea:
"Here am I,
Your special island!
Come to me,
Come to me!"

Your own special hopes,
Your own special dreams,
Bloom on the hillside
And shine in the stream.

If you try,
You'll find me
Where the sky
Meets the sea;

"Here I am,
Your special island!
Come to me,
Come to me!"
Bali Ha'i
Bali Ha'i
Bali Ha'i.

Someday you'll see me,
Floating in the sunshine,
My head sticking out
From a low-flying cloud;
You'll hear me call you,
Singing through the sunshine,
Sweet and clear as can be:
"Come to me,
Here I am,
Come to me!"

Bali Ha'i
Will whisper
On the wind
Of the sea:
"Here am I,
Your special island!
Come to me,
Come to me."

Bali Ha'i
Bali Ha'i
Bali Ha'i.

Baubles, Bangles And Beads

Words & Music by Robert Wright & George Forrest
(Music Based on Themes of A. Borodin)

from *Kismet*

Baubles, bangles,
Hear how they jing-jing-a-ling-a,
Baubles, bangles,
Bright, shiny beads.
Sparkles, spangles,
My heart will sing, sing-a-ling-a,
Wearing baubles, bangles and beads.

I'll glitter and gleam so,
Make somebody dream so
That someday he may
Buy me a ring, ring-a-ling-a,
I've heard that's where it leads,
Wearing baubles, bangles and beads.

Barcelona

Words & Music by Stephen Sondheim

from *Company*

Robert: Where you going?
April: Barcelona.
Robert: Oh,
April: Don't get up.
Robert: Do you have to?
April: Yes, I have to.
Robert: Oh.
April: Don't get up. Now you're angry.
Robert: No, I'm not.
April: Yes, you are.
Robert: No, I'm not. Put your things down.
April: See, you're angry.
Robert: No, I'm not.
April: Yes, you are.
Robert: No, I'm not. Put your wings down and
   stay.
April: I'm leaving.
Robert: Why?
April: To go to...
Robert: Stay.
April: I have to...
Both: Fly.
Robert: I know,
Both: To Barcelona.

Robert:
Look, you're a very special girl,
Not just overnight.
No, you're a very special girl,
And not because you're bright.
Not just because you're bright.
You're just a very special girl, June.
April: April.
Robert: April.
April: Thank you.

Robert: Whatcha thinking?
April: Barcelona.
Robert: Oh.
April: Flight eighteen.
Robert: Stay a minute.
April: I would like to.
Robert: So?
April: Don't be mean.
Robert: Stay a minute.
April: No, I can't.
Robert: Yes, you can.
April: No, I can't.
Robert: Where you going?
April: Barcelona.
Robert: So you said.
April: And Madrid,
Robert: Bon voyage.
April: On a Boeing.
Robert: Good night.
April: You're angry.
Robert: No.
April: I've go to...
Robert: Right.
April: Report to...
Robert: Go.

April:
That's not to say
That if I had my way,
Oh, well, I guess, okay.

Robert: What?
April: I'll stay.
Robert: But...Oh, God!

Beauty & The Beast

Lyrics by Howard Ashman
Music by Alan Menken

from Walt Disney's *Beauty & the Beast*

Tale as old as time,
True as it can be.
Barely even friends,
Then somebody bends
Unexpectedly.

Just a little change.
Small, to say the least.
Both a little scared,
Neither one prepared.
Beauty and the Beast.
Ever just the same.
Ever a surprise.
Ever as before,
Ever just as sure
As the sun will rise.

Tale as old as time.
Tune as old as song.
Bittersweet and strange,
Finding you can change,
Learning you were wrong.

Certain as the sun
Rising in the East.
Tale as old as time,
Song as old as rhyme.
Beauty and the Beast.

Tale as old as time,
Song as old as rhyme
Beauty and the Beast.

Beauty School Dropout

Words & Music by Warren Casey & Jim Jacobs

from *Grease*

Your story's sad to tell,
A teenage ne'er-do-well,
Most mixed up non-delinquent on the block.
Your future's so unclear now,
What's left of your career now?
Can't even get a trade-in on your smock.

Beauty school dropout,
No graduation day for you.
Beauty school dropout,
Missed your mid-terms and
    flunked shampoo.
Well, at least you could have taken time
To wash and clean your clothes up,
After spending all that dough
To have the doctor fix your nose up.

Baby, get movin',
Why keep your feeble hopes alive?
What are ya provin'?
You got the dream but not the drive.
If you go for your diploma,
You could join a steno-pool,
Turn in your teasing comb
And go back to high school.

Beauty school dropout,
Hangin' around the corner store.
Beauty school dropout,
It's about time you knew the score.
Well, they couldn't teach you anything,
You think you're such a looker,
But no customer would go to you,
Unless she was a hooker.

Baby, don't sweat it,
You're not cut out to hold a job.
Better forget it,
Who wants their hair done by a slob?
Now, your bangs are curled,
Your lashes twirled,
But still the world is cruel.
Wipe off that angel face
And go back to high school.

Additional Lyrics:
Baby, you blew it!
You put our good advice to shame.
How could you do it?
Betcha Dear Abby'd say the same.
Guess there's no way to get through to you,
No matter who may try.
Might as well go back
To that malt shop in the sky.
Yah.

Before The Parade Passes By

Music & Lyric by Jerry Herman

from *Hello, Dolly!*

Dolly:
Before the parade passes by,
I'm gonna get in step while there's still time left.
Before the parade passes by…

Before the parade passes by,
I'm gonna go and taste Saturday's high life.
Before the parade passes by,
I'm gonna get some life back into my life.
I'm ready to move out in front.
I've had enough of just passing by life.
With the rest of them,
With the best of them,
I can hold my head up high!
For I've got a goal again,
I've got a drive again,
I'm gonna feel my heart coming alive again,
Before the parade passes by.

Look at that crowd up ahead,
Listen and hear that brass harmony growing.
Look at that crowd up ahead,
Pardon me if my old spirit is showing.
All of those lights over there
Seem to be telling me where I'm going.
When the whistles blow,
And the cymbals crash,
And the sparklers light the sky,
I'm gonna raise the roof,
I'm gonna carry on,
Give me an old trombone,
Give me an old baton,
Before the parade passes by.

Chorus:
When the parade passes by,
Listen and hear that brass harmony
  growing.
When the parade passes by,
Pardon me if my old spirit is showing.
All of those lights over there
Seem to be telling me where I'm going.
When the whistles blow,
And the cymbals crash,
And the sparklers light the sky,
I'm gonna raise the roof,
I'm gonna carry on,
Give me an old trombone,
Give me an old baton.
Before the parade passes by.

I'm gonna raise the roof,
I'm gonna carry on,
Give me an old trombone,
Give me an old baton.
Before the parade passes by.

Being Alive

Words & Music by Stephen Sondheim

from *Company*

Someone to hold you too close,
Someone to hurt you too deep,
Someone to sit in your chair
To ruin your sleep,
To make you aware
Of being alive,
Being alive.

Someone to need you too much,
Someone to know you too well,
Someone to pull you up short,
To put you through hell,
And give you support
Is being alive,
Being alive.

Someone you have to let in,
Someone whose feelings you spare,
Someone who, like it or not,
Will want you to share
A little, a lot,
Is being alive,
Being alive.

Someone to crowd you with love,
Someone to force you to care,
Someone to make you come through,
Who'll always be there
As frightened as you
Of being alive,
Being alive,
Being alive,
Being alive.

Somebody hold me too close,
Somebody hurt me too deep,
Somebody sit in my chair,
And ruin my sleep,
And make me aware
Of being alive.
Being alive.

Somebody need me too much,
Somebody know me too well,
Somebody pull me up short
And put me through hell,
And give me support
For being alive.
Being alive.
Make me alive.
Make me alive.
Make me confused,
Mock me with praise.
Let me be used,
Vary my days.
But alone is alone, not alive.

Somebody crowd me with love,
Somebody force me to care.
Somebody make me come through,
I'll always be here
As frightened as you,
To help us survive,
Being alive,
Being alive,
Being alive.

.

The Best Things In Life Are Free

Words & Music by B.G. DeSylva, Lew Brown & Ray Henderson

from *Good News!*

The moon belongs to ev'ryone,
The best things in life are free.
The stars belong to ev'ryone,
They gleam there for you and me.

The flowers in Spring,
The robins that sing,
The sunbeams that shine,
They're yours, they're mine!

And love can come to ev'ryone,
The best things in life are free.

Big Spender

Music by Cy Coleman
Lyrics by Dorothy Fields

from *Sweet Charity*

The minute you walked in the joint,
I could see you were a man of distinction,
A real Big Spender,
Good looking, so refined.
Say, wouldn't you like to know what's going on
    in my mind?
So let me get right to the point,
I don't pop my cork for ev'ry guy I see.
Hey! Big Spender,
Spend a little time with me.

Wouldn't you like to have fun, fun, fun?
How's about a few laughs, laughs?
I can show you a good time,
Let me show you a good time.

The minute you walked in the joint,
I could see you were a man of distinction,
A real Big Spender,
Good looking, so refined.
Say, wouldn't you like to know what's going on
    in my mind?
So let me get right to the point,
I don't pop my cork for ev'ry guy I see.
Hey! Big Spender,
Hey! Big Spender!
Hey! Big Spender!
Spend a little time with me,
Spend a little time with me,
Spend a little time with me.

The Blue Room

Words by Lorenz Hart
Music by Richard Rodgers

from *The Girl Friend*

All my future plans,
Dear, will not suit your plans.
Read the little blueprints.
Here's your mother's room.
Here's your brother's room.
On the wall are two prints.
Here's the kiddie's room,
Here's the biddy's room,
Here's a pantry lined with shelves, dear.
Here I've planned for us
Something grand for us,
Where we two can be ourselves, dear.

Refrain:
We'll have a blue room,
A new room,
For two room,
Where every day's a holiday,
Because you're married to me.
Not like a ballroom,
A small room,
A hall room,
Where I can smoke my pipe away
With your wee head upon my knee.
We will thrive on,
Keep alive on,
Just nothing but kisses,
With Mister and Missus
On little blue chairs.

You sew your trousseau,
And Robinson Crusoe
Is not so far from worldly cares
As our blue room far away upstairs.

From all visitors
And inquisitors
We'll keep our apartment.
I won't change your plans
You arrange your plans
Just the way your heart meant.
Here we'll be ourselves
And we'll see ourselves
Doing all the things we're scheming.
Here's a certain place,
Cretonne curtain place,
Where no one can see us dreaming.

Refrain

Bring Him Home

Music by Claude-Michel Schönberg
Lyrics by Alain Boublil & Herbert Kretzmer

from *Les Misérables*

God on high,
Hear my prayer.
In my need,
You have always been there.

He is young,
He's afraid.
Let him rest,
Heaven blessed.

Bring him home,
Bring him home,
Bring him home.

He's like the son
I might have known.
If God had granted me a son.
The summers die,
One by one.
How soon they fly,
On and on.
And I am old,
And will be gone.

Bring him peace,
Bring him joy.
He is young,
He is only a boy.

You can take,
You can give,
Let him be,
Let him live.

If I die,
Let me die,
Let him live.
Bring him home.

Broadway Baby

Words & Music by Stephen Sondheim

from *Follies*

I'm just a Broadway Baby,
Walking off my tired feet,
Pounding Forty Second Street
To be in a show.

Broadway Baby,
Learning how to sing and dance,
Waiting for that one big chance
To be in a show.

Gee, I'd like to be
On some marquee,
All twinkling lights,
A spark to pierce the dark
From Batt'ry Park
To Washington Heights.

Some day maybe,
All my dreams will be repaid.
Heck I'd even play the maid
To be in a show.

Say, Mister producer,
Some girls get the breaks.
Just give me my cue, sir,
I've got what it takes.
Say, Mister producer
I'm talkin' to you sir.

I don't need a lot,
Only what I got,
Plus a tube of greasepaint
And a follow spot!

I'm a Broadway Baby,
Slaving at the five and ten,
Dreaming of the great day when
I'll be in a show.
Broadway Baby,
Making rounds all afternoon,
Eating at a greasy spoon
To save on my dough.

At my tiny flat
There's just my cat,
A bed and a chair.
Still I'll stick it till
I'm on a bill
All over Times Square.

Some day maybe,
If I stick it long enough,
I can get to strut my stuff,
Working for a nice man,
Like a Ziegfeld or a Weissman,
In a big-time Broadway show!

Brotherhood Of Man

Words & Music by Frank Loesser

from *How To Succeed In Business Without Really Trying*

Finch:
Now, you may join the Elks, my friend,
And I may join the Shriners.
And other men may carry cards
As members of the Diners.
Still others wear a golden key,
Or small Greek letter pin.
But I have learned there's one great club
That all of us are in.

There is a brotherhood of man,
A benevolent brotherhood of man,
A noble tie that binds
All human hearts and minds
Into one brotherhood of man.

Refrain 1:
Your lifelong membership is free.
Keep a-giving each brother all you can.
Oh, aren't you proud to be
In that fraternity,
The great, big brotherhood of man?

One man may seem incompetent,
Another not make sense,
While others look like quite a waste
Of company expense.
They need a brother's leadership,
So please don't do them in,
Remember mediocrity
Is not a mortal sin.

Finch and Men:
They're [We're] in the brotherhood of man,
Dedicated to giving all we can.
Finch:
Oh, aren't you proud to be
In that fraternity,
Men:
The great, big brotherhood of man?

Womper (Spoken):
No kidding!

Womper (Sung):
Is there really a brotherhood of man?
On the level,
A brotherhood of man?

Biggley and Men:
Yes, you're a brother,
You are a brother!
Oh yes, oh yes.
A noble tie that binds
All human hearts and minds,

Womper:
Into one brotherhood of man.
Men:
Oh, yes.

Men:
Refrain 1

Miss Jones:
You, you got me,
Me, I got you-oo,
You-oo.

Miss Jones:
Refrain 2:
Oh, that noble feeling,
Feels like bells are pealing,
Down with double dealing,
Oh, brother.
You, you got me,
Me, I got you-oo.
You-oo.

Miss Jones and Men:
Refrain 2

Men:
Oh, that noble feeling,
(Oh!)
Feels like bells are pealing,
Down with double dealing,

Miss Jones and Men:
Oh, brother.
You, you got me,
Me, I got you-oo.
You-oo.

All:
Refrain 1

Buddy's Blues

Words & Music by Stephen Sondheim

from *Follies*

Hello, folks, we're into the Follies!
First, though, folks,
   we'll pause for a mo'.
No, no, folks, you'll still get your jollies,
It's just I got a problem that I think you should
   know.

See, I've been very perturbed of late,
   very upset,
Very betwixt and between.
The things that I want
   I don't seem to get.
The things that I get…
You know what I mean?

I've got those
"God, why don't you love me,
Oh you do, I'll see you later"
Blues,
That "Long as you ignore me,
You're the only thing that matters"
Feeling.

Refrain:
That "If I'm good enough for you,
You're not good enough,"
And "Thank you for the present,
But what's wrong with it?" stuff.

Those "Don't come any closer
'Cause you know how much I love you"
Feelings,
Those "Tell me that you love me,
Oh you did, I gotta run now"
Blues.

Spoken:
Margie?

Sung:
She says she really loves me,
(I love you.)
She says.
She says she really cares.
(I care. I care.)
She says that I'm her hero,
(My hero.)
She says.
I'm perfect, she swears.
(You're perfect, goddamn it.)
She says that if we parted,
(If we parted—)
She says,
She says that she'd be sick.
(Bleah.)
She says she's mine forever,
(Forever.)
She says.
I gotta get outta here quick!

I've got those
"Whisper how I'm better than I think,
But what do you know?"
Blues.
That "Why do you keep telling me I stink,
When I adore you?"
Feeling.

That "Say I'm all the world to you,
You're out of your mind,"
"I know there's someone else
And I could kiss your behind,"

Those "You say I'm terrific
But your taste was always rotten"
Feelings,
Those "Go away, I need you,"
"Come to me, I'll kill you,"
"Darling, I'll do anything
To keep you with me till you
Tell me that you love me,
Oh you did, now beat it, will you?"
Blues.

Spoken:
Sally. Oh, Sally.

Sung:
She says she loves another,
(Another.)
She says,
A fella she prefers.
(Furs. Furs.)
She says that he's her idol.
(Idol idol idol idol.)
She says.
"Ideal," she avers.
(You deal. Avers?!)
She says that anybody
(Buddy, Bleah!)
Would suit her more than I.
(Aye, aye, aye.)
She says that I'm a washout,
(A washout!)
She says.
I love her so much I could die!

I've got those
"God, why don't you love me,
Oh you do, I'll see you later"
Blues,
(Bla bla blues,)
That "Long as you ignore me,
You're the only thing that matters"
Feeling.
(Feeling.)

Refrain

Those "Don't come any closer
Cause you know how much I love you"
Feelings,
Those "If you will, then I can't,"
"If you don't, then I gotta,"
"Give it to me, I don't want it,"
"If you won't I gotta have it,"
High, low,
Wrong, right,
Yes, no,
Black, white,
"God, why don't you love me,
Oh you do, I'll see you later"
Blues!

Bui-doi

Music by Claude-Michel Schönberg
Lyrics by Richard Maltby Jr. & Alain Boublil
Adapted from original French lyrics by Alain Boublil.

from *Miss Saigon*

Like all survivors I once thought
When I'm home I won't give a damn,
But now I Know I'm caught.
I'll never leave Vietnam.
War isn't over when it ends,
Some pictures never leave your mind.
They are the faces of the children,
The ones we left behind.

They're called Bui-doi.
The dust of life,
Conceived in hell and born in strife.
They are the living reminder
Of all the good we failed to do.
We can't forget, must not forget
That they are our children too.

Those kids hit walls on ev'ry side,
They don't belong in any place.
Their hist'ry they can't even hide,
It's written on their face.
I never thought one day I'd pleed
For half-breeds from a land that's torn.
But then I saw a camp for children,
Whose crime was being born.

They're called Bui-doi.
The dust of life,
Conceived in hell and born in strife.
We owe them fathers and a family,
A loving home they never knew.
Because we know deep in our hearts
That they are all our children too.

These are souls in need, they need us to give.
Someone has to pay for their chance to live.

John:
Help me try.

Men's Chorus:
They're called Bui-Doi.
The dust of life,
Conceived in hell and born in strife.

Men's Chorus & John:
They are the living reminder of
All the good we failed to do.
That's why we know
Deep in our hearts

John:
That they are our children too.

A Bushel And A Peck

By Frank Loesser

from *Guys & Dolls*

I love you a bushel and a peck,
A bushel and a peck and a hug around the
    neck,
Hug around the neck and a barrel and a heap,
Barrel and a heap and I'm talkin' in my sleep
About you,
About you.

Refrain:
'Cause I love you a bushel and a peck,
Y'bet your purty neck I do.
Doodle oodle oodle,
Doodle oodle oodle,
A-doodle oodle oodle ooo.

I love you a bushel and a peck,
A bushel and a peck, tho' you make my heart a
    wreck,
Make my heart a wreck and you make my life a
    mess,
Make my life a mess, yes a mess of happiness,
About you,
About you.

Refrain

I love you a bushel and a peck,
A bushel and a peck and it beats me all to
    heck,
Beats me all to heck how I'll ever tend the
    farm,
Ever tend the farm when I wanna keep my arm
About you,
About you.

Refrain

Button Up Your Overcoat

Words & Music by B.G. DeSylva, Lew Brown & Ray Henderson

from *Follow Thru*

Refrain:
Button up your overcoat,
When the wind is free,
Take good care of yourself,
You belong to me!

Eat an apple ev'ry day,
Get to bed by three,
Take good care of yourself,
You belong to me!

Be careful crossing streets,
Oo-oo!
Don't eat meats,
Oo-oo!
Cut out sweets,
Oo-oo!
You'll get a pain
And ruin your tum-tum!

Keep away from bootleg hootch,
When you're on a spree,
Take good care of yourself,
You belong to me!

Refrain

Wear your flannel underwear,
When you climb a tree,
Take good care of yourself,
You belong to me!

Don't sit on hornets' tails,
Oo-oo!
Or on nails,
Oo-oo!
Or third rails,
Oo-oo!
You'll get a pain
And ruin your tum-tum!

Don't go out with college boys,
When you're on a spree,
Take good care of yourself,
You belong to me.

Bye Bye Baby

Words by Leo Robin
Music by Jule Styne

from *Gentlemen Prefer Blondes*

I'll be in my room alone
Ev'ry Post Meridian,
And I'll be with my diary
And that book by Mister Gideon.

Refrain:
Bye bye baby!
Remember you're my baby
When they give you the eye.
Although I know that you care,
Won't you write and declare
That though on the loose,
You are still on the square.

I'll be gloomy,
But send that rainbow to me,
Then my shadows will fly,
Though you'll be gone for awhile,
I know that I'll be smiling
With my baby, bye and bye.

Refrain

With my baby, bye and bye.

Cabaret

Words by Fred Ebb
Music by John Kander

from *Cabaret*

What good is sitting alone in your room?
Come hear the music play;
Life is a cabaret, old chum,
Come to the cabaret.

Put down your knitting, the book and the
   broom,
Time for a holiday;
Life is a cabaret, old chum,
Come to the cabaret.

Come taste the wine,
Come hear the band.
Come blow the horn, start celebrating;
Right this way your table's waiting.

No use permitting some prophet of doom,
To wipe every smile away;
Life is a cabaret, old chum.
Come to the cabaret.

I used to have a girlfriend known as Elsie,
With whom I shared four sordid rooms in
   Chelsea.
She wasn't what you'd call a blushing flower,
As a matter of fact she rented by the hour.
The day she died the neighbors came to
   snicker:
"Well, that's what comes of too much pills and
   liquor."

But when I saw her laid out like a queen,
She was the happiest corpse I'd ever seen.
I think of Elsie to this very day.
I remember how she'd turn to me and say:

What good is sitting alone in your room?
Come hear the music play;
Life is a cabaret, old chum,
Come to the cabaret.

Put down your knitting, the book and the
   broom,
Time for a holiday;
Life is a cabaret, old chum,
Come to the cabaret.

And as for me, as for me,
I made my mind up back in Chelsea,
When I go I'm going like Elsie.

Start by admitting from cradle to tomb
Isn't that long a stay;
Life is a cabaret, old chum,
Only a cabaret, old chum
And I love a cabaret.

C'est Magnifique

Words & Music by Cole Porter

from *Can-Can*

Love is such a fantastic affair,
When it comes to call,
After taking you up in the air,
Down it lets you fall.
But be patient and soon you will find,
If you follow your heart, not your mind,
Love is waiting there, again,
To take you up in the air, again.

Refrain:
When love comes in,
And takes you for a spin,
Oo-la-la-la,
C'est magnifique.
When ev'ry night
Your loved one holds you tight,
Oo-la-la-la,
C'est magnifique.
But when, one day,
Your loved one drifts away,
Oo-la-la-la,
It is so tragique.
But when, once more,
He [She] whispers,
"Je t'adore,"
C'est magnifique.

Refrain

Additional Lyrics:
Verse 2:
When you began of love to speak,
I followed every word.
But when you called love magnifique,
I would have called it absurd.
And when you said it was often tragique,
I would have said it was always comique.
So, mad'moiselle, be sweet to me,
And kindly do not repeat to me.

Camelot

Words by Alan Jay Lerner
Music by Frederick Loewe

from *Camelot*

A law was made a distant moon ago here,
July and August cannot be too hot.
And there's a legal limit to the snow here,
In Camelot.

The winter is forbidden till December,
And exits March the second on the dot.
By order summer lingers
   through September,
In Camelot.

Camelot! Camelot!
I know it sounds a bit bizarre,
But in Camelot, Camelot,
That's how conditions are.

The rain may never fall till after sundown.
By eight the morning fog must disappear.
In short, there's simply not
A more congenial spot,
For happily-ever-aftering
Than here in Camelot!

The winter is forbidden till December,
And exits March the second on the dot.
By order summer lingers
   through September,
In Camelot.

Camelot! Camelot!
I know it gives a person pause,
But in Camelot, Camelot,
Those are the legal laws.

The snow may never slush upon the hillside.
By nine P.M. the moonlight must appear.
In short, there's simply not
A more congenial spot
For happily-ever-aftering
Than here in Camelot.

Can You Feel The Love Tonight?

Music by Elton John
Lyrics by Tim Rice

from Walt Disney's *The Lion King*

There's a calm surrender
To the rush of day,
When the heat of the rolling world
Can be turned away.
An enchanted moment,
And it sees me through.
It's enough for this restless warrior
Just to be with you.

Refrain:
And can you feel the love tonight?
It is where we are.
It's enough for this wide-eyed wanderer
That we got this far.
And can you feel the love tonight,
How it's laid to rest?
It's enough to make kings and vagabonds
Believe the very best.

There's a time for everyone,
If they only learn,
That the twisting kaleidoscope
Moves us all in turn.
There's a rhyme and reason
To the wild outdoors,
When the heart of this star-crossed voyager
Beats in time with yours.

Refrain

Can't Help Lovin' Dat Man

Music by Jerome Kern
Words by Oscar Hammerstein II

from *Showboat*

Fish got to swim and birds got to fly,
I got to love one man till I die,
Can't help lovin' dat man of mine.
Tell me he's lazy, tell me he's slow,
Tell me I'm crazy maybe I know,
Can't help lovin' dat man of mine.

When he goes away
Dat's a rainy day,
And when he comes back dat day is fine,
De sun will shine.

He can come home as late as can be,
Home widout him ain't no home to me,
Can't help lovin' dat man of mine.

Caravan

Words & Music by Duke Ellington, Irving Mills & Juan Tizol

from *Sophisticated Ladies*

Night and stars above that shine so bright,
The mystery of their fading light,
That shines upon our caravan.

Sleep upon my shoulder as we creep
Across the sands so I may keep,
This memory of our caravan.

This is so exciting
You are so inviting
Resting in my arms
As I thrill to the magic charms of you,

Beside me here beneath the blue
My dream of love is coming true
Within our desert caravan.

Castle On A Cloud

Music by Claude-Michel Schönberg
Original Lyrics by Alain Boublil & Jean-Marc Natel
English Lyrics by Herbert Kretzmer

from *Les Misérables*

There is a castle on a cloud.
I like to go there in my sleep.
Aren't any floors for me to sweep,
Not in my castle on a cloud.

There is a room that's full of toys.
There are a hundred boys and girls.
Nobody shouts or talks too loud,
Not in my castle on a cloud.

There is a lady all in white,
Holds me and sings a lullaby.
She's nice to see and she's soft to touch.
She says, "Cosette, I love you very much."

I know a place where no one's lost.
I know a place where no one cries.
Crying at all is not allowed,
Not in my castle on a cloud.

Chiquitita

Words & Music by Benny Andersson & Björn Ulvaeus

from *Mamma Mia!*

Rosie:
Chiquitita, tell me, what's wrong?

Tanya:
I have never seen such sorrow

Rosie/Tania:
In your eyes, and the wedding
Is tomorrow.

Tanya:
How I hate to see you like this.

Rosie:
There is no way you can deny it;

Tanya:
I can see that you're oh so sad,
So quiet.

Rosie/Tanya:
Chiquitita, tell me the truth,
I'm a shoulder you can cry on.
Your best friend, I'm the one you
Must rely on.

You were always sure of yourself,
Now I see you've broken a feather,
I hope we can
Patch it up together.

Chiquitita, you and I know,
How the heartaches come and they go
And the scars they're leavin'
We'll be dancing once again,
And the pain will end,
You will have no time for grievin'.

Chiquitita, you and I cry,
But the sun is still in the sky
And shining above you.
Let me hear you sing once more,
Like you did before,
Sing a new song Chiquitita.

Donna:
Try once more,
Like I did before,
Sing a new song Chiquitita.

Circle Of Life

Music by Elton John
Lyrics by Tim Rice

from Walt Disney's *The Lion King*

From the day we arrive on the planet
And blinking, step into the sun,
There's more to be seen than can ever be seen,
More to do than can ever be done.

Some say, "Eat or be eaten."
Some say, "Live and let live."
But all are agreed
As they join the stampede,
You should never take more than you give
In the circle of life.

Refrain:
It's the wheel of fortune.
It's the leap of faith.
It's the band of hope
Till we find our place
On the path unwinding
In the circle of life.

Some of us fall by the wayside,
And some of us soar to the stars.
And some of us sail through our troubles,
And some have to live with the scars.
There's far too much to take in here,
More to find than can ever be found.
But the sun rolling high
Through the sapphire sky
Keeps great and small on the endless round
In the circle of life.

Refrain Twice

On the path unwinding
In the circle,
The circle of life.

Class

Words by Fred Ebb
Music by John Kander

from *Chicago*

What ever happened to fair dealing,
And pure ethics and nice manners?
Why is it ev'ryone now is a pain in the ass?
What ever happened to class?
Class!

What ever happened to "please, may I?"
And "yes, thank you," and "how charming!"
Now ev'ry son of a bitch is a snake in the grass.
What ever happened to class?
Class!

Ah, there ain't no gentlemen to open up the
    doors,
There ain't no ladies now there's only pigs and
    whores,
And even kids'll knock ya down so's they can
    pass.
Nobody's got no class.

What ever happened to old values,
And fine morals, and good breeding?
Now no one even says "oops,"
When they're passing their gas.
What ever happened to class?
Class!

Ah, there ain't no gentlemen who's fit for any
    use,
And any girl'd touch your privates for a deuce.
And even kids'll kick your shins and give you
    sass.
Nobody's got no class.

All you read about today is rape and theft.
Jesus Christ!
Ain't there no decency left?
Nobody's got no class.

Ev'rybody you watch
S'got his brains in his crotch.
Holy crap (holy crap),
What a shame (what a shame).
What's become of class?

Climb Ev'ry Mountain

Lyrics by Oscar Hammerstein II
Music by Richard Rodgers

from *The Sound Of Music*

Climb every mountain,
Search high and low,
Follow every byway,
Every path you know.

Climb every mountain,
Ford every stream,
Follow every rainbow,
Till you find your dream!

A dream that will need
All the love you can give,
Every day of your life
For as long as you live.

Climb every mountain,
Ford every stream,
Follow every rainbow
Till you find your dream!

Close As Pages In A Book

Words by Dorothy Fields
Music by Sigmund Romberg

from *Up In Central Park*

We'll be close as pages in a book,
My love and I.
So close we can share a single look,
Share every sigh.

So close that before I hear your laugh,
My laugh breaks through;
And when a tear starts to appear,
My eyes grow misty too.

Our dreams won't come tumbling to the
    ground.
We'll hold them fast.
Darling, as the strongest book is bound,
We're bound to last.

Your life is my life and while life beats away in
    my heart,
We'll be as close as pages in a book.

Comedy Tonight

Words & Music by Stephen Sondheim

from *A Funny Thing Happened On The Way To The Forum*

Something familiar, something peculiar,
Something for everyone, a comedy tonight!
Something appealing, something appalling.
Something for everyone, a comedy tonight!

Nothing with kings, nothing with crowns.
Bring on the lovers, liars and clowns!
Old situations, new complications,
Nothing portentous or polite;
Tragedy tomorrow, comedy tonight!

Something convulsive, something repulsive,
Something for everyone, a comedy tonight!
Something esthetic, something frenetic,
Something for everyone, a comedy tonight.

Nothing of Gods, nothing of Fate.
Weighty affairs will just have to wait.
Nothing that's formal, nothing that's normal,
No recitations to recite!
Open up the curtain, comedy tonight.

Consider Yourself

Words & Music by Lionel Bart

from *Oliver!*

Consider yourself at home.
Consider yourself one of the family.
We've taken to you so strong,
It's clear we're going to get along.

Consider yourself well in.
Consider yourself part of the furniture.
There isn't a lot to spare.
Who cares, whatever we've got, we share.

If it should chance to be we should
    see some harder days,
Empty larder days, why grouse?
Always a chance to meet somebody to
    foot the bill,
Then drinks are on the house.

Consider yourself our mate.
We don't want to have no fuss.
For after some consideration we can state,
Consider yourself one of us.

Consider yourself at home.
Consider yourself one of the family.
We've taken to you so strong,
It's clear we're going to get along.

Consider yourself well in.
Consider yourself part of the furniture.
There isn't a lot to spare.
Who cares, whatever we've got, we share.

Nobody tries to be lah-di-dah and uppity.
There's a cup of tea for all.
Only it's wise to be handy wiv' a rolling pin
When the landlord comes to call!

Consider yourself our mate.
We don't want to have no fuss.
For after some consideration we can state,
Consider yourself one of us.

Could I Leave You?

Words & Music by Stephen Sondheim

from *Follies*

Leave you? Leave you?
How could I leave you?
How could I go it alone?
Could I wave the years away,
With a quick good-bye?
How do you wipe tears away,
When your eyes are dry?

Sweetheart, lover,
Could I recover,
Give up the joys I have known?
Not to fetch your pills again,
Ev'ry day at five,
Not to give those dinners for ten
Elderly men from the U.N.,
How could I survive?

Could I leave you,
And your shelves of the World's Best Books,
And the evenings of martyred looks,
Cryptic sighs,
Sullen glares from those injured eyes?
Leave the quips with a sting,
Jokes with a sneer,
Passionless lovemaking, once a year?
Leave the lies,
Ill concealed,
And the wounds never healed
And the games not worth winning,
And—wait! I'm just beginning!

What, leave you? Leave you?
How could I leave you?
What would I do on my own?
Putting thoughts of you aside,
In the south of France,
Would I think of suicide?
Darling, shall we dance?

Could I live through the pain
On a terrace in Spain?
Would it pass?
It would pass.
Could I bury my rage
With a boy half your age,
In the grass?
Bet your ass.

But I've done that already.
Or didn't you know, love?
Tell me, how could I leave,
When I left long ago, love?
Could I leave you?
No, the point is,
Could you leave me?
Well, I guess you could
Leave me the house,
Leave me the flat,
Leave me the Braques and Chagalls
And all that.

You could leave me the stocks,
For sentiment's sake,
And ninety percent
Of the money you make,
And the rugs,
And the cooks,
Darling you keep the drugs,
Angel, you keep the books,
Honey, I'll take the grand,
Sugar, you keep the spinet
And all of our friends and…
Just wait a goddamn minute!

Oh, leave you? Leave you?
How could I leave you?
Sweetheart, I have to confess.
Could I leave you?
Yes.
Will I leave you?
Will I leave you?

(Spoken:)
Guess!

Dancing Queen

Words & Music by Benny Andersson, Björn Ulvaeus & Stig Anderson

from *Mamma Mia!*

Rosie/Tanya:
Ooh, you can dance, you can jive,
Having the time of your life,
Ooh, see that girl, watch that scene,
Diggin' the Dancing Queen.

Friday night and the lights are low,
Looking out for a place to go;
Where they play the right music,
Getting in the swing,
You come to look for a king.

Tanya:
Anybody can be that guy.
Night is young and the music's high.
With a bit of rock music,
Everything is fine,
You're in the mood for dance.
And when you get the chance.

Donna/Rosie/Tanya:
You are the Dancing Queen
Young and sweet only seventeen
Dancing Queen,
Feel the beat from the tambourine, oh yeah.
You can dance, you can jive,
Having the time of your life,
Ooh, see that girl, watch that scene,
Diggin' the Dancing Queen.

Donna:
You're a teaser, you turn 'em on,
Leave 'em burning and then you're gone,
Lookin' out for another
Anyone will do,
You're in the mood for dance.
And when you get the chance.

Donna/Tanya/Rosie:
You are the Dancing Queen
Young and sweet only seventeen
Dancing Queen,
Feel the beat from the tambourine, oh yeah.
You can dance, you can jive,
Having the time of your life,
Ooh, see that girl, watch that scene,
Diggin' the dancing queen.

See that girl, watch that scene,
Diggin' the dancing queen!

Diamonds Are A Girl's Best Friend

Words by Leo Robin
Music by Jule Styne

from *Gentlemen Prefer Blondes*

A kiss on the hand may be quite continental,
But diamonds are a girl's best friend.
A kiss may be grand but it won't pay the rental
On your humble flat,
Or help you at the Automat.
Men grow cold as girls grow old
And we all lose our charms in the end.
But square cut or pear-shape,
These rocks don't lose their shape,
Diamonds are a girl's best friend.

There may come a time when a lass needs a
    lawyer,
But diamonds are a girl's best friend.
There may come a time when a hard-boiled employer
    employer
Thinks you're awful nice,
But get that "ice" or else no dice.
He's your guy when stocks are high,
But beware when they start to descend.
It's then that those louses go back to their
    spouses,
Diamonds are a girl's best friend.

Do I Hear A Waltz?

Music by Richard Rodgers
Lyrics by Stephen Sondheim

from *Do I Hear A Waltz?*

Do I hear a waltz?
Very odd, but I hear a waltz.
There isn't a band,
And I don't understand it at all.

I can't hear a waltz.
Oh my Lord, there it goes again!
Why is nobody dancing in the street?
Can't they hear the beat?

Refrain:
Magical, mystical miracle!
Can it be? Is it true?
Things are impossibly lyrical!
Is it me? No, it's you!

I do hear a waltz!
I see you and I hear a waltz!
It's what I've been waiting for.
An old lady is waltzing in her flat,
Waltzing with her cat!

Roses are dancing with peonies!
Yes, it's true! Can't you see?
Ev'rything's suddenly Viennese!
Can't be you! Must be me!

Do I hear a waltz?
I want more than to hear a waltz!
I want you to share it 'cause,
Oh, boy, do I hear a waltz?

Refrain

I hear a waltz!

Do I Love You
Because You Are Beautiful?

Words & Music by Oscar Hammerstein II & Richard Rodgers

from *Cindarella*

Do I love you
Because you're beautiful,
Or are you beautiful
Because I love you?
Am I making believe I see you,
A girl too lovely to
Be really true?
Do I want you
Because you're wonderful?
Or are you wonderful
Because I want you?
Are you the sweet invention of a lover's dream?
Or are you really as beautiful as you seem?

Do You Hear The People Sing?

Music by Claude-Michel Schönberg
Original Lyrics by Alain Boublil & Jean-Marc Natel
English Lyrics by Herbert Kretzmer

from *Les Misérables*

Refrain:
Do you hear the people sing,
Singing the song of angry men?
It is the music of a people
Who will not be slaves again!
When the beating of your heart
Echoes the beating of the drums,
There is a life about to start
When tomorrow comes.

Will you join in our crusade?
Who will be strong and stand with me?
Beyond the barricade,
Is there a world you long to see?
Then join in the fight
That will give you the right to be free!

Refrain

Will you give all you can give,
So that our banner may advance?
Some will fall and some will live.
Will you stand up and take your chance?
The blood of the martyrs
Will water the meadows of France!

Refrain

Don't Cry For Me Argentina

Music by Andrew Lloyd Webber
Lyrics by Tim Rice

from *Evita*

Eva:
It won't be easy, you'll think it strange
When I try to explain how I feel,
That I still need your love
After all that I've done:
You won't believe me
All you will see is a girl you once knew
Although she's dressed up to the nines
At sixes and sevens with you.

I had to let it happen, I had to change;
Couldn't stay all my life down at heel:
Looking out of the window,
Ataying out of the sun.
So I chose freedom
Running around trying everything new,
But nothing impressed me at all,
I never expected it to.

Refrain:
Don't cry for me Argentina
The truth is I never left you:
All through my wild days,
My mad existence,
I kept my promise,
Don't keep your distance.

And as for fortune and as for fame
I never invited them in:
Though it seemed to the world
They were all I desired.
They are illusions,
They're not the solutions they promised to be,
The answer was here all the time
I love you and hope you love me.

Don't cry for me Argentina
Mm…

Refrain

Have I said too much?
There's nothing more I can think of
To say to you.
But all you have to do is look at me
To know that ev'ry word is true.

Don't Rain On My Parade

Words by Bob Merrill
Music by Jule Styne

from *Funny Girl*

Don't tell me not to live,
Just sit and putter.
Life's candy and the sun's
A ball of butter.
Don't bring around a cloud
To rain on my parade!

Don't tell me not to fly,
I've simply got to.
If someone takes a spill,
It's me and not you.
Who told you you're allowed
To rain on my parade?

Refrain:
I'll march my band out,
I'll beat my drum.
And if I'm fanned out,
Your turn at bat, sir,
At least I didn't fake it.
Hat, sir!
I guess I didn't make it.

But whether I'm the rose
Of sheer perfection,
Or freckle on the nose
Of life's complexion,
The cinder or the shiny apple
Of its eye,

I gotta fly once,
I gotta try once,
Only can die once.
Right, sir?
Ooh, love is juicy,
Juicy and you see
I gotta have my bite, sir!

Get ready for me, love,
'Cause I'm a "comer."
I simply gotta march,
'Cause I'm a drummer.
Don't bring around a cloud
To rain on my parade.

I'm gonna live and live now!
Get what I want I know how.
One roll for the whole shebang!
One throw, that bell will go clang!
Eye on the target and wham!
One shot, one gun shot and bam!
Hey, Mister Arnstein,
Here I am!

Refrain

Get ready for me, love,
'Cause I'm a "comer."
I simply gotta march,
My heart's a drummer.
Nobody, no, nobody
Is gonna rain on my parade!

Do-Re-Mi

Lyrics by Oscar Hammerstein II
Music by Richard Rodgers

from *The Sound of Music*

Let's start at the very beginning,
A very good place to start.
When you read you begin with—
A, B, C.
When you sing you begin with do re mi.

Do re mi?

Do re mi.

The first three notes just happen to be
Do Re Mi.
Doe—a deer, a female deer,
Ray—a drop of golden sun,
Me—a name I call myself,
Far—a long, long way to run,
Sew—a needle pulling thread,
La—a note to follow sew,
Tea—a drink with jam and bread.
That will bring us back to do!

Do re mi fa so la ti do.

Drink With Me

Music by Claude-Michel Schönberg
Lyrics by Alain Boubil & Herbert Kretzmer

from *Les Misérables*

Drink with me to days gone by.
Sing with me the songs we knew.
Here's to pretty girls
Who went to our heads,
Here's to witty girls
Who went to our beds,
Here's to them
And here's to you!

Drink with me to days gone by.
To the life that used to be.
At the shrine of friendship
Never say die!
Let the wine of friendship
Never run dry.
Here's to you.
And here's to me.

To the life that used to be
At the shrine of friendship
Never say die!
Let the wine of friendship
Never run dry.
Here's to you.
And here's to me.

Edelweiss

Lyrics by Oscar Hammerstein II
Music by Richard Rodgers

from *The Sound Of Music*

Edelweiss
Edelweiss
Ev'ry morning you greet me.
Small and white
Clean and bright,
You look happy to meet me.

Blossom of snow
May you bloom and grow,
Bloom and grow forever.

Edelweiss
Edelweiss
Bless my homeland forever.

Elaborate Lives

Music by Elton John
Lyrics by Tim Rice

from Walt Disney Theatrical Productions' *Aida*

Radames:
We all lead such elaborate lives,
Wild ambitions in our sights.
How an affair of the heart survives,
Days apart and hurried nights.
Seems quite unbelievable to me.
I don't want to live like that.
Seems quite unbelievable to me.
I don't want to love like that.
I just want our time to be
Slower and gentler,
Wiser, free.

We all live in extravagant times,
Playing games we can't all win.
Unintended emotional crimes.
Take some out, take others in.
I'm so tired of all we're going through.
I don't want to live like that.
I'm so tired of all we're going through.
I don't want to love like that.
I just want to be with you,
Now and forever,
Peaceful, true.

This may not be the moment
To tell you face to face,
But I could wait forever
For the perfect time and place.

Radames & Aida:
We all lead such elaborate lives.
We don't know whose words are true.
Strangers, lovers, husbands, wives,
Hard to know who's loving who.
Too many choices tear us apart.
I don't want to live like that.

Radames:
Too many choices
Tear us apart.
I don't want to love like that,
I just want to touch your heart.
May this confession
Both:
Be the start.

Empty Chairs At Empty Tables

Music by Claude-Michel Schönberg
Lyrics by Alain Boublil & Herbert Kretzmer

from *Les Misérables*

There's a grief that can't be spoken,
There's a pain goes on and on,
Empty chairs at empty tables,
Now my friends are dead and gone.

Here they talked of revolution,
Here it was they lit the flame,
Here they sang about tomorrow,
And tomorrow never came.

From the table in the corner,
They could see a world reborn,
And they rose with voices ringing.
And I can hear them now.
The very words that they had sung
Became their last communion,
On the lonely barricade at dawn.

Oh, my friends, my friends, forgive me,
That I live, and you are gone,
There's a grief that can't be spoken,
There's a pain goes on and on.

Phantom faces at the window,
Phantom shadows on the floor.
Empty chairs at empty tables,
Where my friends will meet no more.

Oh, my friends, my friends, don't ask me
What your sacrifice was for.
Empty chairs at empty tables
Where my friends will sing no more.

Ev'ry Time We Say Goodbye

Words & Music by Cole Porter

from *Seven Lively Arts*

Ev'ry time we say goodbye
I die a little.
Ev'ry time we say goodbye
I wonder why a little.
Why the gods above me
Who must be in the know
Think so little of me
They allow you to go.

When you're near there's such an air
Of Spring about it,
I can hear a lark somewhere
Begin to sing about it.
There's no love song finer,
But how strange the change from major to
    minor,
Ev'ry time we say goodbye.
Ev'ry single time
We say goodbye.

Everything's Coming Up Roses

Words by Stephen Sondheim
Music by Jule Styne

from *Gypsy*

I had a dream,
A dream about you, Baby!
It's gonna come true, Baby!
They think that we're through,
But Baby.

You'll be swell,
You'll be great,
Gonna have the whole world on a plate.
Starting here,
Starting now,
Honey, everything's coming up roses!

Clear the decks,
Clear the tracks,
You got nothing to do but relax,
Blow a kiss,
Take a bow,
Honey, everything's coming up roses!

Now's your inning,
Stand the world on its ear!
Set it spinning,
That'll be just the beginning!

Curtain up,
Light the lights,
You got nothing to hit but the heights!
You'll be swell,
You'll be great!
I can tell, just you wait!
That lucky star I talk about is due!
Honey, everything's coming up roses for me and
    for you!

You can do it,
All you need is a hand.
We can do it,
Momma is gonna see to it!

Curtain up!
Light the lights!
We got nothing to hit but the heights!
I can tell,
Wait and see,
There's the bell,
Follow me!
And nothing's gonna stop us till we're through!
Honey, everything's coming up roses and
    daffodils,
Everything's coming up sunshine and
    Santa Claus,
Everything's gonna be bright-lights and
    lollipops.
Everything's coming up roses for me and for
    you.

Everybody Ought To Have A Maid

Words & Music by Stephen Sondheim

from *A Funny Thing Happened On The Way To The Forum*

Ev'rybody ought to have a maid.
(Ev'rybody ought to have a maid.)
Ev'rybody ought to have a working girl.
Ev'rybody ought to have a lurking girl,
To putter around the house.

Ev'rybody ought to have a maid.
(Ev'rybody ought to have a maid.)
Ev'rybody ought to have a menial,
Consistently congenial,
And quieter than a mouse.

Refrain:
Oh! Oh!
Wouldn't she be delicious,
Tidying up the dishes,
Neat as a pin?
Oh! Oh!
Wouldn't she be delightful,
Sweeping out?
Sleeping in?

Ev'rybody ought to have a maid!
(Ev'rybody ought to have a maid!)
Someone whom you hire when
   you're short of help,
To offer you the sort of help
You never get from a spouse.

Fluttering up the stairway,
Shuttering up the windows,
Cluttering up the bedroom,
Buttering up the master,
Puttering all around the house.

Refrain

Ev'rybody ought to have a maid.
Someone who, when fetching you your slipper
   will
Be winsome as a whippoorwill,
And graceful as a grouse.

Skittering down the hallway,
Flittering thru the parlor,
Tittering in the pantry,
Littering up the bedroom,
Puttering all around…
The house!

Additional Lyrics

Encore 1:
Ev'rybody ought to have a maid.
Ev'rybody ought to have a serving girl,
A loyal and unswerving girl,
Who's quieter than a mouse.Oh! Oh!
Think of her at the dust bin,
'Specially when she's just been
Traipsing about.
Oh! Oh!
Wouldn't she be delightful,
Living in,
Giving out?

Ev'rybody ought to have a maid.
Tidily collecting bits of paper 'n' strings,
Appealing in her apron strings,
Beguiling in her blouse!

Puttering thru the attic,
Chattering in the cellar,
Clattering in the kitchen,
Flattering in the bedroom,
Puttering all around...
The house!

Encore 2:
Ev'rybody ought to have a maid.
Someone who's efficient and reliable,
Obedient and pliable,
And quieter than a mouse.

Oh! Oh!
Wouldn't she be so nimble,
Fiddling with her thimble,
Mending a gown?
Oh! Oh!
Wouldn't she be delightful,

Cleaning up,
Leaning down!

Ev'rybody ought to have a maid,
Someone who'll be busy as a bumblebee,
And even if you grumble, be
As graceful as a grouse!

Wriggling in the anteroom,
Jiggling in the living room,
Giggling in the dining room,
Wiggling in the other rooms,
Puttering all around...
The house!

Falling In Love With Love

Words by Lorenz Hart
Music by Richard Rodgers

from *The Boys From Syracuse*

I weave with brightly colored strings
To keep my mind off other things;
So, ladies, let your fingers dance,
And keep your hands out of romance.
Lovely witches,
Let the stitches
Keep your fingers under control.
Cut the thread, but leave
The whole heart whole.
Merry maids can sew and sleep;
Wives can only sew and weep!

Refrain:
Falling in love with love
Is falling for make-believe.
Falling in love with love
Is playing the fool.
Caring too much is such
A juvenile fancy.
Learning to trust is just
For children in school.
I fell in love with love
One night when the moon was full.
I was unwise, with eyes
Unable to see.
I fell in love with love,
With love everlasting,
But love fell out with me.

A Fellow Needs A Girl

Lyrics by Oscar Hammerstein II
Music by Richard Rodgers

from *Allegro*

A fellow needs a girl
To sit by his side
At the end of a weary day,
To sit by his side
And listen to him talk
And agree with the things he'll say.

A fellow needs a girl
To hold in his arms
When the rest of his world goes wrong,
To hold in his arms
And know that she believes
That her fellow is wise and strong.

When things go right
And his job's well done,
He wants to share
The prize he's won.
(If no one shares,
And no one cares,
Where's the fun
Of a job well done
Or a prize you've won?)

A fellow needs a home,
His own kind of home,
But to make this dream come true
A fellow needs a girl,
His own kind of girl…
My kind of girl is you.

Fugue For Tinhorns

Words & Music by Frank Loesser

from *Guys & Dolls*

I got the horse right here,
The name is Paul Revere.
And here's a guy that says if the weather's clear,
Can do, can do,
This guy says the horse can do.
If he says the horse can do,
Can do, can do.

For Paul Revere I'll bite
I hear his foot's alright.
Of course it all depends if it rained last night.
Likes mud, likes mud,
This X means the horse likes mud.
If that means the horse likes mud,
Likes mud, likes mud.

I tell you Paul Revere,
Now this is no bum steer.
It's from a handicapper that's real sincere.
Can do, can do,
This guy says the horse can do.
If he says the horse can do,
Can do, can do.

Epitaph, Valentine, Paul Revere,
I got the horse right here.

Get Me To The Church On Time

Words by Alan Jay Lerner
Music by Frederick Loewe

from *My Fair Lady*

I'm getting married in the morning.
Ding! Dong! The bells are gonna chime.
Pull out the stopper;
Let's have a whopper;
But get me to the church on time!
I gotta be there in the morning;
Spruced up and looking in my prime.
Girls, come out and kiss me;
Show how you'll miss me,
But get me to the church on time!

If I am dancing,
Roll up the floor!
If I am whistling,
Whewt me out the door!
For I'm getting married in the morning.
Ding! Dong! The bells are gonna chime.
Kick up a rumpus,
But don't lose the compass,
And get me to the church,
Get me to the church,
For Gawd's sake,
Get me to the church on time.

Gaston

Lyrics by Howard Ashman
Music by Alan Menken

from Walt Disney's *Beauty & The Beast*

LeFou:
Gosh, it disturbs me to see you, Gaston,
Looking so down in the dumps.
Ev'ry guy here'd like to be you, Gaston,
Even when taking your lumps.
There's no man in town as admired as you.
You're ev'ryone's favorite guy.
Ev'ryone's awed and inspired by you,
And it's not very hard to see why.
No one's slick as Gaston.
No one's quick as Gaston.
No one's neck's as incredibly thick as Gaston's.
For there's no man in town half as manly.
Perfect! A pure paragon.
You can ask any Tom, Dick or Stanley,
And they'll tell you whose team they prefer to
    play on.

Chorus:
No one's been like Gaston,
A kingpin like Gaston,

LeFou:
No one's got a swell cleft in his chin like
    Gaston.

Gaston:
As a specimen, yes, I'm intimidating!

Chorus:
My, what a guy, that Gaston!
Give five "hurrahs!"
Give twelve "hip-hips!"

LeFou:
Gaston is the best and the rest is all drips!

Men:
No one fights like Gaston,
Douses lights like Gaston,

LeFou:
In a wrestling match, nobody bites like Gaston.

Women:
For there's no one as burly and brawny.

Gaston:
As you see, I've got biceps to spare.

LeFou:
Not a bit of him's scraggly or scrawny.

Gaston:
That's right!
And ev'ry last inch of me's covered with hair.

Chorus:
No one hits like Gaston, matches wits like
    Gaston,

LeFou:
In a spitting match, nobody spits like Gaston.

Gaston:
I'm especially good at expectorating. Ptooey!

Chorus:
Ten points for Gaston!

Gaston:
When I was a lad I ate four dozen eggs
Ev'ry morning to help me get large.
And now that I'm grown, I eat five dozen eggs,
So I'm roughly the size of a barge!

Chorus:
No one shoots like Gaston,
Makes those beauts like Gaston.
Then goes tromping around in his boots like
    Gaston.

Gaston:
I use antlers in all of my decorating!
Chorus:

My, what a guy,
Gaston!

Gethsemane (I Only Want To Say)

Words & Music by Andrew Lloyd Webber

from *Jesus Christ Superstar*

I only want to say,
If there is a way,
Take this cup away from me
For I don't want to taste its poison,
Feel it burn me, I have changed,
I'm not as sure
As when we started.

Then I was inspired
Now I'm sad and tired.
Listen, surely I've exceeded expectations?
Tried for three years, seems like thirty.
Could you ask as much from any other man?

But if I die
See the saga through
And do the things you ask of me.
Let them hate me,
Hit me, hurt me,
Nail me to their tree.

I'd wanna know, I'd wanna know my God.
I'd wanna know, I'd wanna know my God.
I'd wanna see, I'd wanna see my God.
I'd wanna see, I'd wanna see my God.

Why I should die?
Would I be more noticed
Than I ever was before?
Would the things I've said and done
Matter any more?

I'd have to know, I'd have to know my Lord.
I'd have to know, I'd have to know my Lord.
I'd have to see, I'd have to see my Lord.
I'd have to see, I'd have to see my Lord.

If I die what will be my reward?
If I die what will be my reward?
I'd have to know, I'd have to know my Lord
I'd have to know, I'd have to know my Lord

Why should I die?
Why should I die?

Can you show me now
That I would not be killed in vain?
Show me just a little
Of your omnipresent brain.

Show me there's a reason
For your wanting me to die.
You're far too keen on where and how
And not so hot on why.

Alright I'll die!
Just watch me die!
See how I die!
See how I die!

Then I was inspired
Now I'm sad and tired.
After all, I've tried for three years.
Seems like ninety.
Why then am I
Scared to finish what I started?
What you started- I didn't start it.

God thy will is hard
But you hold ev'ry card
I will drink your cup of poison,
Nail me to your cross and break me.
Bleed me, beat me, kill me, take me
Now, before I change my mind.

Getting To Know You

Lyrics by Oscar Hammerstein II
Music by Richard Rodgers

from *The King & I*

It's a very ancient saying,
But a true and honest thought,
That "if you become a teacher
By your pupils you'll be taught."
As a teacher I've been learning
(You'll forgive me if I boast)
And I've now become an expert
On the subject I like most:

Getting to know you.
Getting to know all about you,
Getting to like you,
Getting to hope you like me.
Getting to know you,
Putting it my way, but nicely,
You are precisely
My cup of tea!

Getting to know you,
Getting to feel free and easy;
When I am with you,
Getting to know what to say,
Haven't you noticed?
Suddenly I'm bright and breezy
Because of
All the beautiful and new
Things I'm learning about you,
Day by day.

Gonna Build A Mountain

Words & Music by Leslie Bricusse & Anthony Newley

from *Stop The World, I Want To Get Off!*

Gonna build a mountain from a little hill.
Gonna build a mountain, least I hope I will.
Gonna build a mountain; gonna build it high.
I don't know how I'm gonna do it;
Only know I'm gonna try.

Gonna build a daydream from a little hope.
Gonna push that daydream up the mountain
   slope.
Gonna build a daydream; gonna see it through.
Gonna build a mountain and a daydream;
Gonna make 'em both come true.

Gonna build a heaven from a little hell.
Gonna build a heaven and I know darn well.
If I build my mountain with a lot of care.
And take my daydream up the mountain
Heaven will be waiting there.

When I've built that heaven, as I will someday,
And the Lord sends Gabriel to take me away,
Wanna a fine young son to take my place.
I'll leave a son in my heaven on earth,
With the Lord's good grace.

With a fine young son to take my place
I'll leave a son in my heaven on earth
With the Lord's good grace.

Guys & Dolls

Words & Music by Frank Loesser

from *Guys & Dolls*

What's playing at the Roxy?
I'll tell you what's playing at the Roxy.
A picture about a Minnesota man,
So in love with a Mississippi girl
That he sacrifices everything
And moves all the way to Biloxi.
That's what's playing at the Roxy.

What's in the Daily News?
I'll tell you what's in the Daily News,
Story about a guy
Who bought his wife a small ruby,
With what otherwise would have been
His union dues.
That's what's in the Daily News.

What's happening all over?
I'll tell you what's happening all over.
Guys sitting home by a television set,
Who once used to be something of a rover,
That's what's happening all over.
Love is the thing that has lick'd 'em.
And it looks like Nathan's
     just another victim.

(Spoken): Yes sir!

(Sung):
When you see a guy reach for stars in the sky,
You can bet that he's doing it for some doll.
When you spot a John waiting out in the rain,
Chances are he's insane as only a John can be
     for a Jane.
When you meet a gent paying all kinds of rent,
For a flat that could flatten the Taj Mahal,

Call it sad, call it funny,
But it's better than even money,
That the guy's only doing it for some doll.

When you see a Joe saving half of his dough,
You can bet there'll be mink in it for some doll,
When a bum buys wine like a bum can't afford,
It's a cinch that the bum is under the thumb of
     some little broad.
When you meet a mugg lately out of the jug,
And he's still lifting platinum folderol,
Call it hell, call it heaven,
It's a probable twelve to seven,
That the guy's only doing it for some doll.

When you see a sport and his cash has
     run short,
Make a bet that he's banking it with some doll.
When a guy wears tails with the
     front gleaming white,
Who the hell do you think he's tickling pink
On Saturday night?
When a lazy slob takes a good steady job,
And he smells from Vitalis and Barbasol,
Call it dumb, call it clever,
Ah, but you can give it odds forever,
That the guy's only doing it for some doll, some
     doll, some doll,
The guy's only doing it for some doll!

Hakuna Matata

Music by Elton John
Lyrics by Tim Rice

from Walt Disney's *The Lion King*

Timon:
Hakuna matata…
What a wonderful phrase!

Pumbaa:
Hakuna matata…
Ain't no passing craze.

Timon:
It means no worries
For the rest of your days.

Timon & Pumbaa:
It's a problem-free philosophy.

Timon:
Hakuna matata.

Why, when he was a young warthog….

Pumbaa:
When I was a young warthog!

Timon (Spoken):
Very nice.

Pumbaa (Spoken):
Thanks.

Timon:
He found his aroma
Lacked a certain appeal.
He could clear the savannah
After every meal!

Pumbaa:
I'm a sensitive soul,
Though I seem think-skinned.
And it hurt that my friends
Never stood downwind!
Ah, oh the shame!

Timon:
He was ashamed!

Pumbaa:
Thought of changing my name!

Timon:
Oh, what's in a name?

Pumbaa:
And I got downhearted…

Timon:
How did you feel?

Pumbaa:
Every time that I…

Timon (Spoken):
Hey Pumbaa!

Not infront of the kids!

Pumbaa (Spoken):
Oh, sorry.

Timon & Pumba (Sung):
Hakuna matata....

What a wonderful phrase:

Hakuna matata....

Ain't no passing craze.

Simba:
It means no worries

For the rest of your days.

Timon & Simba:
It's our problem-free

Pumbaa:
Philosophy.

All:
Hakuna matata.

Happiness

Words & Music by Clark Gesner

from *You're A Good Man, Charlie Brown*

Happiness is two kinds of ice cream,
Finding your skate key,
Telling the time.

Happiness is learning to whistle,
Tying your shoe,
For the very first time.

Happiness is playing the drum
In your own school band.
And happiness is walking,
Hand in hand.

Happiness is finding a nickel,
Catching a firefly,
Setting him free.

Happiness is being alone,
Ev'ry now and then.
And happiness is coming home,
Again.

Happiness is having a sister,
Sharing a sandwich,
Getting along.

Happiness is singing together,
When day is through.
And happiness is those
Who sing with you.

Happiness is morning and evening,
Daytime and nighttime, too,
For happiness is anyone,
And anything at all
That's loved by you.

Have You Met Miss Jones?

Words by Lorenz Hart
Music by Richard Rodgers

from *I'd Rather Be Right*

It happened, I felt it happen.
I was awake, I wasn't blind.
I didn't think, I felt it happen.
Now I believe in matter over mind.
And you see we mustn't wait.
The nearest moment that we marry is too late!

"Have you met Miss Jones?"
Someone said as we shook hands.
She was just Miss Jones to me.
Then I said, "Miss Jones,
You're a girl who understands
I'm a man who must be free."
And all at once I lost my breath.
And all at once was scared to death.
And all at once I owned the earth and sky!
Now I've met Miss Jones
And we'll keep on meeting till we die,
Miss Jones and I.

Heaven Help My Heart

Words & Music by Benny Andersson, Tim Rice & Björn Ulvaeus

from *Chess*

If it were love I would give that love
Every second I had, and I do.
Did I know where he'd lead me to?
Did I plan doing all of this
For the love of a man?

Well, I let it happen anyhow
And what I'm feeling now
Has no easy explanation.
Reason plays no part,
Heaven, help my heart.

I love him too much.
What if he saw my whole existence
Turning around
A word, a smile, a touch?

One of these days, and it won't be long,
He'll know more about me than he should.
All my dreams will be understood,
No surprise, nothing more to learn
From the look in my eyes.

Don't you know that time is not my friend,
I'll fight it to the end,
Hoping to keep that best of moments
When the passions start.
Heaven help my heart.

The day that I find
Suddenly I've run out of secrets,
Suddenly I'm not always on his mind.

Maybe it's best to love a stranger,
Well, that's what I've done
Heaven help my heart.

Heaven help my heart.

Heaven On Their Minds

Words & Music by Andrew Lloyd Webber

from *Jesus Christ Superstar*

My mind is clearer now
At last, all too well, I can see
Where we all soon will be.
If you strip away the myth from the man
You will see where we all soon will be.

Jesus!
You've started to believe the things they say of
    you,
You really do believe this talk of God is true.
And all the good you've done will soon get
    swept away
You've begun to matter more than the things
    you say.

Listen Jesus, I don't like what I see.
All I ask is that you listen to me,
And remember
I've been your right hand man all along.
You have set them all on fire.
They think they've found the new Messiah.
And they'll hurt you when they find they're
    wrong.

I remember when this whole thing began;
No talk of God then we called you a man.
And believe me my admiration for you hasn't
    died.
But every word you say today
Gets twisted 'round some other way,
And they'll hurt you if they think you've lied.

Nazareth, your famous son
Should have stayed a great unknown,
Like his father carving wood-
He'd have made good.
Tables, chairs and oaken chests
Would have suited Jesus best,
He'd have caused nobody harm,
No one alarm.

Listen Jesus do you care for your grace?
Don't you see we must keep in our place?
We are occupied
Have you forgotten how put down we are?
I am frightened by the crowd,
For we are getting much too loud.
And they'll crush us if we go too far.

Listen Jesus to the warning I give
Please remember that I want us to live,
But it's sad to see our chances weakening with
    ev'ry hour.
All your followers are blind,
Too much heaven on their minds.
It was beautiful but now it's sour.
Yes, it's all gone sour.

Ah ah ah ah ah (*Repeat & fade*)

A Heart Full Of Love

Music by Claude-Michel Schönberg
Original Lyrics by Alain Boublil & Jean-Marc Natel
English Lyrics by Herbert Kretzmer

from *Les Misérables*

Marius:
A heart full of love!
A heart full of song
I'm doing everything all wrong
Oh God, for shame,
I do not even know your name!
Dear Mad'moiselle,
I am lost in your spell.
A heart full of love!
A heart full of you!
The words are foolish but they're true:
Cosette! Cosette!
Or were we dreaming when we met?

Cosette:
Who can say?
Who can tell?
A heart full of love!
A heart full of you!
I saw you waiting and I knew.
Waiting for you.

Marius:
At your feet.

Cosette:
At your call.

Both:
And it isn't a dream,
Not a dream after all.

Hello, Young Lovers

Lyrics by Oscar Hammerstein II
Music by Richard Rodgers

from *The King & I*

When I think of Tom
I think about a night
When the earth smelled of summer
And the sky was streaked with white,
And the soft mist of England
Was sleeping on a hill,
I remember this
And I always will.
There are new lovers now
On the same silent hill
Looking on the same blue sea,
And I know Tom and I
Are a part of them all
And they're all a part of Tom and me.

Hello, young lovers,
Whoever you are,
I hope your troubles are few
All my good wishes go with you tonight
I've been in love like you.
Be brave, young lovers, and follow your star,
Be brave and faithful and true.
Cling very close to each other tonight
I've been in love like you.

I know how it feels
To have wings on your heels,
And to fly down a street in a trance
You fly down a street
On a chance that you'll meet,
And you meet
Not really by chance.

Don't cry young lovers,
Whatever you do,
Don't cry because I'm alone.
All of my memories are happy tonight!
I've had a love of my own,
I've had a love of my own like yours,
I've had a love of my own.

The Heat Is On In Saigon

Music by Claude-Michel Schönberg
Lyrics by Richard Maltby Jr. & Alain Boublil
Adapted from original French lyrics by Alain Boublil

from *Miss Saigon*

Americans:
The heat is on in Saigon,
The girls are hotter 'n hell
One of these slits here will be Miss Saigon.
God the tension is high
Not to mention the smell,
The heat is on in Saigon.

A Marine:
Is there a war going on?
Don't ask I ain't gonna tell

Chris:
How are you doing there John?

John:
I got the hots for Yvonne,
We should get drunk and get laid
Since the end is so near.

Chris:
I tell you Buddy I've had it,
I don't want to hear.

John:
The heat is on in Saigon,
But 'til they tell me I'm gone
I'm gonna buy you a girl.

Chris:
You can buy me a beer.

Kim:
I'm seventeen and I'm new here today,
The village I come from seems so far away.
All of the girls know much more what to say.
But I know I have a heart like the sea,
A million dreams are in me.

Chris:
Good Jesus John who is she?

Americans:
The Cong is tight'ning the noose,
Is it a week or a day or an hour that we get?
Tonight could be our last shot,
Got to put it to use.

American Men & Girls:
Tonight I bet
That you and I will get along.
Forget about the threat,
Forget the Vietcong

American Men:
Mimi, Gigi, Yvette or Yvonne,
Gonna buy me a beer and elect Miss Saigon.

Engineer (spoken):
Attention s'il vous plaît!
By popular demand, Miss Gigi Van Tranh, is
    crowned Miss Saigon!

American Men:
The heat is on in Saigon
And things are not going well
But still at midnight the party goes on
And goodbye party in hell.

Hello, Dolly!

Music & Lyric by Jerry Herman

from *Hello, Dolly!*

Dolly:
Hello, Harry,
Well, hello, Louie,
It's so nice to be back home where I belong.
You're lookin' swell, Danny,
I can tell, Manny,
You're still glowin', you're still crowin',
You're still goin' strong.
I feel the room swayin',
For the band's playin'
One of my old fav'rite songs from 'way back
   when.
So, bridge that gap, fellas,
Find me an empty lap, fellas,
Dolly'll never go away again!

Men:
Hello, Dolly,
Well, hello, Dolly,
It's so nice to have you back where you belong.
You're lookin' swell, Dolly,
We can tell, Dolly,
You're still glowin', you're still crowin',
You're still goin' strong.
We feel the room swayin',
For the band's playin'
One of your old fav'rite songs from 'way back
   when. So,

Dolly:
Here's my hat, fellas,
I'm stayin' where I'm at, fellas.
Men:
Promise you'll never go away again!

Dolly:
I went away from the lights of Fourteenth Street,
And into my personal haze.
But now that I'm back in the lights of
   Fourteenth Street,
Tomorrow will be brighter than the good old
   days.
Men:
Those good old days!

Hello, Dolly,
Well, hello (hey, look, there's) Dolly.

Dolly:
(*Spoken*) Glad to see you,
(*Sung*) Hank, let's thank my lucky star.
(Your lucky star.)
(*Spoken*) You're lookin' great, Stanley,
Lose some weight, Stanley?
(*Sung*) Dolly's overjoyed and overwhelmed,
And over par.

Men:
I hear the ice tinkle,
See the lights twinkle,
And you still get glances from us handsome
　　men. So,

Dolly:
Golly gee, fellas,
Find me a vacant knee, fellas,

Men:
Dolly'll never go away again.

Men:
Well, well, hello, Dolly,
Well, hello, Dolly,
It's so nice to have you back where you belong.
You're lookin' swell, Dolly,
We can tell, Dolly,
You're still glowin', you're still crowin',
You're still goin' strong.
I hear the ice tinkle,
See the lights twinkle,
And you still get glances from us handsome
　　men. So,

Dolly:
Wa,wa, wow, fellas,
Look at the old girl now, fellas,
Men:
Dolly'll never go away again!

High Flying, Adored

Music by Andrew Lloyd Webber
Lyrics by Tim Rice

from *Evita*

Che:
High flying, adored, so young
The instant queen,
A rich beautiful thing, of all the talents
A cross between
A fantasy of the bedroom and a saint.
And you were just a back street girl,
Hustling and fighting
Scratching and biting.

High flying, adored,
Did you believe in your wildest moments
All this would be yours,
That you'd become the lady of them all?

Were the stars in your eyes
When you crawled in at night
From the bars, from the sidewalks,
From the gutter theatrical?
Don't look down, it's a long way to fall.

High flying, adored what happens now?
Where do you go from here?
For someone on top of the world
The view's not exactly clear,
A shame you did it all at twenty six.
There are no mysteries now;
Nothing can thrill you,
No one fulfill you.

High flying, adored,
I hope you come to terms with boredom
So famous, so easily, so soon,
Is not the wisest thing to be.

You won't care if they love you,
It's been done before.
You'll despair if they hate you,
You'll be drained of all energy,
All the young who've made it would agree.

Eva:
High flying, adored,
I've been called names
but they're the strangest.
My story's quite usual
Local girl makes good,
Weds famous man
I was slap in the right place
At the perfect time
Filled a gap, I was lucky.
But one thing I'll say for me
No one else can fill it like I can.

Honey Honey

Words & Music by Benny Andersson, Björn Ulvaeus & Stig Anderson

from *Mamma Mia!*

Sophie:
Honey, honey, how he thrills me, ah ha,
Honey, honey.
Honey, honey, nearly kills me, ah ha,
Honey, honey.

I'd heard about him before,
I wanted to hear some more.
And now I know what they mean,
He's a love machine.
(Oh, he makes me dizzy!)

Honey, honey, let me feel it, ah ha,
Honey honey.
Honey, honey don't conceal it, ah ha,
Honey, honey.

The way that you kiss good night,
The way that you hold me tight,
I feel like I wanna sing
When you do your...... thing.

Sophie (Spoken):
I want my dad to give me away at my wedding
But according to Mum's diary,
I've got three possible dads;
Sam, Bill or Harry.

Ali:
Sophie!

Lisa:
Do they know?

Sophie:
Well what do you write to a total stranger?
"Come to my wedding, you might be my dad"?

No, they think Mum sent the invitations.
And after reading this diary, I'm not surprised
    they all said yes.

Sophie/Lisa/Ali:
Honey, honey, how you thrill me, ah ha,
Honey, honey.
Honey, honey, nearly kill me, ah ha,
Honey, honey.

Sophie:
I'd heard about you before,
I wanted to know some more.
And now I'm about to see
What you mean to me.

Honeysuckle Rose

Words by Andy Razaf
Music by Thomas "Fats" Waller

from *Ain't Misbehavin'*

Every honey bee fills with jealousy
When they see you out with me.
I don't blame them, goodness knows,
Honeysuckle Rose.

When you're passin' by,
Flowers droop and sigh,
And I know the reason why;
You're much sweeter, goodness knows.

Don't buy sugar, you just have to touch my cup.
You're my sugar, it's sweet when you stir it up.
When I'm takin' sips from your tasty lips,
Seems the honey fairly drips.
You're confection, goodness knows,
Honeysuckle Rose.

Hosanna

Music by Andrew Lloyd Webber
Lyrics by Tim Rice

from *Jesus Christ Superstar*

Crowd:
Hosanna Hey-sanna Sanna Sanna

Hosanna Hey-sanna Hosanna

Hey J.C. , J.C. won't you smile at me?

Sanna Hosanna Hey Superstar!

Caiaphas:
Tell this rabble to be quiet

We anticipate a riot,

This common crowd

Is much too loud.

Tell the mob who sing your song

That they are fools and they are wrong.

They are a curse,

They should disperse.

Crowd:
Hosanna Hey-sanna Sanna Sanna

Hosanna Hey-sanna Hosanna

Hey J.C. , J.C. you're alright by me,

Sanna Hosanna Hey Superstar!

Jesus:
Why waste your breath moaning at the crowd?

Nothing can be done to stop the shouting

If ev'ry tongue was silent the noise would still continue,

The rocks and stones themselves would start to sing:

Crowd, with Jesus:
Hosanna Hey-sanna Sanna Sanna

Hosanna Hey-sanna Hosanna

Crowd:
Hey J.C. , J.C. won't you fight for me?

Sanna Hosanna Hey Superstar

How To Handle A Woman

Words by Alan Jay Lerner
Music by Frederick Loewe

from *Camelot*

Spoken:
You swore that you had taught me
Ev'rything from A to Zed,

Sung:
With nary an omission in between.
Well, I shall tell you what
You obviously forgot:
That's how a ruler rules a queen!
And what of teaching me
By turning me to animal and bird,
From beaver to the smallest bobolink!
I should have had a whirl
At changing to a girl,
To learn the way the creatures think!

But wasn't there a night,
On a summer long gone by,
We pass'd a couple wrangling away;
And did I not say, Merlyn,
What if that chap were I?
And did he not give counsel and say…
What was it now?
My mind's a wall.
Oh, yes!
By jove, now I recall:

How to handle a woman?
There's a way, said the wise old man;
A way known by ev'ry woman
Since the whole rig'marole began.

Do I flatter her?
I begged him answer.
Do I threaten or cajole or plead?
Do I brood or play the gay romancer?
Said he, smiling:
No indeed.

How to handle a woman?
Mark me well, I will tell you, Sir:
The way to handle a woman
Is to love her, simply love her,
Merely love her…love her…love her.

I Ain't Down Yet

Words & Music by Meredith Willson

from *The Unsinkable Molly Brown*

Spoken:
Now looka here,
I am important to me!
I ain't no bottom to no pile.
I mean much more to me
Than I mean to anybody I ever knew!
Certainly more than I mean to any
Si-wash yazzi-hampers like you guys.
Go ahead! Break muh arm!
Me say Uncle? Heh!
Doesn't make a bit-a diff'rence
For you to keep sayin' I'm down, till
Sung:
I say so, too.

Spoken:
J'ever try steppin' on a pissant?
Well, there's one now!
Jump him! Stomp him!
You thinkin' you got him?
Thinkin' he's quit?
Well, he don't think so.
There he goes!
And you can be positive sure,
I'm as good as any pissant that ever lived!
Oh, I hate that word "down,"
But I love the word "up,"
'Cause "up" means hope
An' that's just what I got.

Hope for some place better,
Some place, I dunno,
Cleaner, shinier.
Hell, if I gotta eat catfish heads all my life,
Can't I have 'em offa plate once?
And a red silk dress,
Sung:
When there's girl enough on me to wear one.
And then, someday,
With all my might and all my main,
I'm goan' to:

Learn to read and write.
I'm goan' to see what there is to see.
So, if you go from nowhere
On the road to somewhere,
And you meet anyone,
You'll know it's me.

Spoken:
I'm goan' to
Sung:
Move from place to place,
To find a house with a golden stair.
And if that house is red,
And has a big brass bed,
I'm livin' there!

I Am What I Am

Music & Lyrics by Jerry Herman

from *La Cage Aux Folles*

I am what I am,
I am my own
Special creation,
So, come take a look,
Give me the hook,
Or the ovation.

It's my world,
That I want to have a little pride in,
My world,
And it's not a place I have to hide in.

Refrain:
Life's not worth a damn,
'Til you can say, "Hey world,
I am what I am."

I am what I am,
I don't want praise,
I don't want pity.
I bang my own drum,
Some think it's noise,
I think it's pretty.

And so what,
If I love each feather and each spangle,
Why not
Try and see things from a diff'rent angle?

[Or:]
It's my song,
And if you don't like the style I bring it,
My song,
So at least respect my right to sing it.

Your life is a sham,
'Til you can shout out loud,
"I am what I am."

I am what I am,
And what I am
Needs no excuses,
I deal my own deck,
Sometimes the ace,
Sometimes the deuces.

There's one life,
And there's no return and no deposit,
One life,
So it's time to open up your closet.

[Or:]
It's high time
That I blow my horn and sound my trumpet.
High time,
And if you don't like it, you can lump it.

Refrain

I Believe In You

Words & Music by Frank Loesser

from *How To Succeed In Business Without Really Trying*

You have the cool clear eyes
Of a seeker of wisdom and truth,
Yet, there's that up turned chin
And the grin of impetuous youth.
Oh, I believe in you,
I believe in you.

I hear the sound of good
Solid judgment whenever you talk,
Yet, there's the bold, brave spring
Of the tiger that quickens your walk.
Oh, I believe in you,
I believe in you.

And when my faith in my fellow man
All but falls apart,
I've but to feel your hand grasping mine
And I take heart,
I take heart.

To see the cool clear eyes
Of a seeker of wisdom and truth,
Yet there's that slam bang tang
Reminiscent of gin and vermouth.
Oh, I believe in you,
I believe in you.

I Could Have Danced All Night

Words by Alan Jay Lerner
Music by Frederick Loewe

from *My Fair Lady*

I could have danced all night!
I could have danced all night!
And still have begged for more.
I could have spread my wings
And done a thousand things
I've never done before.

I'll never know what made it so exciting.
Why all at once my heart took flight.
I only know when he began to dance with me
I could have danced and danced all night.

I Could Write A Book

Words by Lorenz Hart
Music by Richard Rodgers

from *Pal Joey*

A B C D E F G
I never learned to spell,
At least not well.
1 2 3 4 5 6 7
I never learned to count
A great amount.
But my busy mind is burning
To use what learning I've got.
I won't waste any time,
I'll strike while the iron is hot.

Refrain:
If they asked me, I could write a book
About the way you walk and whisper and look.
I could write a preface on how we met
So the world would never forget.
And the simple secret of the plot
Is just to tell them that I love you a lot.
Then the world discovers as my book ends
How to make two lovers of friends.

Used to hate to go to school.
I never cracked a book;
I played the hook.
Never answered any mail;
To write I used to think
Was wasting ink.
It was never my endeavor
To be too clever and smart.
Now I suddenly feel
A longing to write in my heart.

Refrain

I Didn't Know What Time It Was

Words by Lorenz Hart
Music by Richard Rodgers

from *Too Many Girls*

Once I was young
Yesterday, perhaps
Danced with Jim and Paul
And kissed some other chaps.
Once I was young,
But never was naïve.
I thought I had a trick or two
Up my imaginary sleeve.
And now I know I was naïve.

Refrain:
I didn't know what time it was,
Then I met you.
Oh, what a lovely time it was,
How sublime it was, too!
I didn't know what day it was.
You held my hand.
Warm like the month of May it was,
And I'll say it was grand.
Grand to be alive, to be young,
To be mad, to be yours alone!
Grand to see your face, feel your touch,
Hear your voice say I'm all your own.
I didn't know what year it was.

Life was no prize.
I wanted love and here it was
Shining out of your eyes.
I'm wise,
And I know what time it is now.

Once I was old
Twenty years or so
Rather well preserved
The wrinkles didn't show.
Once I was old,
But not too old for fun.
I used to hunt for little girls
With my imaginary grin.
But now I aim for only one!

Refrain

I Do Not Know A Day I Did Not Love You

Lyrics by Martin Charnin
Music by Richard Rodgers

from *Two By Two*

I do not know a day I did not love you.
I can't remember love not being there.
The planting, when the earth ran through your
    fingers,
The harvest when the sun danced in your hair.

I do not know a day I did not need you,
For sharing ev'ry moment that I spent.
I needed you before I ever knew you,
Before I knew what needing someone meant.

And if we ever were to have tomorrow,
One fact alone is full (and filled with song),
You will not know a day I do not love you,
The way that I have loved you all along.

I Don't Care Much

Words by Fred Ebb
Music by John Kander

from *Cabaret*

I don't care much.
Go or stay.
I don't care very much,
Either way.

Hearts grow hard
On a windy street.
Lips grow cold,
With the rent to meet.
So if you kiss me,
If we touch,
Warning's fair,
I don't care very much.

Words sound false
When your coat's too thin,
Feet don't waltz
When the roof caves in.
So if you kiss me,
If we touch,
Warning's fair,
I don't care very much.

I Don't Know How To Love Him

Music by Andrew Lloyd Webber
Lyrics by Tim Rice

from *Jesus Christ Superstar*

I don't know how to love him,
What to do, how to move him.
I've been changed, yes really changed.
In these past few days when I've seen myself
I seem like someone else.

I don't know how to take this,
I don't know why he moves me.
He's a man, he's just a man.
And I've had so many men before
In very many ways he's just one more.

Should I bring him down,
Should I scream and shout,
Should I speak of love
Let my feelings out?
I never thought I'd come to this,
What's it all about?

Don't you think it's rather funny
I should be in this position?
I'm the one who's always been
So calm so cool, no lover's fool,
Running ev'ry show.
He scares me so.

Yet if he said he loved me
I'd be lost I'd be frightened,
I couldn't cope, just couldn't cope.
I'd turn my head, I'd back away,
I wouldn't want to know.
He scares me so.
I want him so.
I love him so.

I Dreamed A Dream

Music by Claude-Michel Schönberg
Original Lyrics by Alain Boublil & Jean-Marc Natel
English Lyrics by Herbert Kretzmer

from *Les Misérables*

I dreamed a dream in days gone by,
When hope was high and life worth living.
I dreamed that love would never die.
I dreamed that God would be forgiving.

Then I was young and unafraid,
And dreams were made and used and wasted.
There was no ransom to be paid,
No song unsung, no wine untasted.

But the tigers come at night,
With their voices soft as thunder.
As they tear your hope apart,
As they turn your dream to shame.

He slept a summer by my side.
He filled my days with endless wonder.
He took my childhood in his stride.
But he was gone when autumn came.

And still I dreamed he'd come to me,
That we would live the years together.
But there are dreams that cannot be,
And there are storms we cannot weather.

I had a dream my life would be
So different from this hell I'm living,
So different now from what it seemed.
Now life has killed the dream I dreamed.

I Enjoy Being A Girl

Lyrics by Oscar Hammerstein II
Music by Richard Rodgers

from *Flower Drum Song*

I'm a girl and by me that's only great!
I am proud that my silhouette is curvy,
That I walk with a sweet and girlish gait,
With my hips kind of swively and swervy.
I adore being dressed in something frilly
When my date comes to get me at my place.
Out I go with my Joe or John or Billy,
Like a filly who is ready for the race!

When I have a brand new hair-do,
With my eyelashes all in curl,
I float as the clouds on air do,
I enjoy being a girl!

When men say I'm cute and funny,
And my teeth aren't teeth, but pearl,
I just lap it up like honey,
I enjoy being a girl!

I flip when a fellow sends me flowers,
I drool over dresses made of lace,
I talk on the telephone for hours
With a pound and a half of cream upon my
   face!

I'm strictly a female female,
And my future, I hope, will be
In the home of a brave and free male
Who'll enjoy being a guy,
Having a girl like me!

When men say I'm sweet as candy
As around in a dance we whirl,
It goes to my head like brandy,
I enjoy being a girl!

When someone with eyes that smoulder,
Says he loves every silken curl
That falls on my ivory shoulder,
I enjoy being a girl!

When I hear the complimentary whistle
That greets my bikini by the sea,
I turn and I glower and I bristle
But I'm happy to know the whistle's meant for
   me!

I'm strictly a female female,
And my future, I hope, will be
In the home of a brave and free male
Who'll enjoy being a guy,
Having a girl like me.

I Found A Million Dollar Baby
(In A Five And Ten Cent Store)

Music by Harry Warren
Lyric by Billy Rose & Mort Dixon

from *Crazy Quilt*

Love comes along like a popular song,
Anytime or anywhere at all.
Rain or sunshine, spring or fall,
You never know when it may say hello
In a very unexpected place
For example, take my case:

Refrain 1:
It was a lucky April shower,
It was the most convenient door;
I found a million dollar baby
In a five and ten cent store.

Refrain 2:
The rain continued for an hour,
I hung around for three or four,
Around a million dollar baby
In a five and ten cent store.

Refrain 3:
She was selling china
And when she made those eyes
I kept buying china
Until the crowd got wise.

Refrain 4:
Incidentally, if you run into a shower,
Just step inside my cottage door
And meet the million dollar baby
From the five and ten cent store!

Love used to be quite a stranger to me
Didn't know a sentimental word,
Thoughts of kissing seemed absurd.
Then came a change
And you may think it strange,
But the world became a happy tune
Since that April afternoon.

Repeat Refrains

I Have A Dream

Words & Music by Benny Andersson & Björn Ulvaeus

from *Mamma Mia!*

Sophie:
I have a dream
A song to sing
To help me cope
With anything.

If you see the wonder
Of a fairy tale
You can take the future
Even if you fail.

I believe in angels
Something good in everything I see.
I believe in angels
When I know the time is right for me
I'll cross the stream.
I have a dream.

Company:
I have a dream
A fantasy,
To help me through
Reality.

And my destination
Makes it worth the while,
Pushing through the darkness
Still another mile.

I believe in angels
Something good in everything I see.
I believe in angels.
When I know the time is right for me
I'll cross the stream
I have a dream.
I'll cross the stream

Sophie:
I have a dream.
I'll cross the stream
I have a dream.

I Know Him So Well

Words & Music by Benny Andersson, Tim Rice & Björn Ulvaeus

from *Chess*

Florence:
Nothing is so good it lasts eternally,
Perfect situations must go wrong.
But this has never yet prevented me
Wanting far too much for far too long.

Looking back I could have played it differently,
Won a few more moments, who can tell?
But it took time to understand the man.
Now at least I know I know him well.

Refrain:
Florence:
Wasn't it good?

Svetlana:
Oh, so good.

Florence:
Wasn't he fine?

Svetlana:
Oh, so fine.

Florence:
Isn't it madness

Both:
He can't be mine?

Florence:
But in the end he needs a little more than me,

Svetlana:
More security.

Florence:
He needs his fantasy and freedom.

Both:
I know him so well.

Svetlana:
No one in your life is with you constantly,
No one is completely on your side.
And though I move my world to be with him,
Still the gap between us is too wide.

Looking back I could have played it differently,

Florence:
Looking back I could have played things some
    other way,

Svetlana:
Learned about the man before I fell,

Florence:
I was just a little careless, maybe,

Svetlana:
But I was ever so much younger then,

Florence:
I was so much younger then,
Now at least

Both:
I know I know him well.

Florence:
Wasn't it good?

Svetlana:
Oh, so good.

Florence:
Wasn't he fine?

Svetlana:
Oh, so fine.

Florence:
Isn't it madness

Both:
He won't be mine?

Florence:
Didn't I know how it would go?

If I knew from the start

Why am I falling apart?

Florence:
Wasn't it good?

Svetlana:
Oh, so good.

Florence:
Wasn't he fine?

Svetlana:
Oh, so fine.

Florence:
Isn't it madness

Both:
He won't be mine?

Both:
He won't be mine?

Florence:
But in the end he needs a little bit more than
   me,

Svetlana:
More security.

Florence:
He needs his fantasy and freedom.

Svetlana:
It took time to understand him.

Both:
I know him so well.

I Just Can't Wait To Be King

Music by Elton John
Lyrics by Tim Rice

from Walt Disney's *The Lion King*

Simba:
I'm gonna be a might king
So enemies beware!

Zazu:
Well, I've never seen a king of beasts
With quite so little hair.

Simba:
I'm gonna be the mane event
Like no king was before.
I'm brushing up on looking down.
I'm working on my roar!

Zazu:
Thus far, a rather uninspiring thing.

Simba:
Oh, I just can't wait to be king!

Zazu (Spoken):
You've rather a long way to go young Master!
If you think....

Simba:
No one saying "do this,"

Zazu (Spoken):
Now, when I said that I....

Simba:
No one saying "be there,"

Zazu (Spoken):
What I meant was that the.....

Simba:
No one saying "Stop that!"

Zazu (Spoken):
But what you don't realise....

Simba:
No one saying "See here,"

Zazu (Spoken):
Now see here!

Simba:
Free to run around all day,

Zazu (Spoken):
Well that's definitely out!

Simba:
Free to do it all my way!

Zazu:
I think it's time that you and I
Arranged a heart to heart.

Simba:
Kings don't need advice from little
Hornbills for a start.

Zazu:
If this is where the monarchy is headed,
Count me out!
Our of service, out of Africa,
I wouldn't hang about.
This child is getting wildly out of wing!

Simba:
Oh, I just can't wait to be king!

Everybody look left,
Everybody look right.
Everywhere you look
I'm standing in the spot light.

Zazu:
Not yet!

Simba & Chorus:
Let every creature go for broke and sing.
Let's hear it in the herd and on the wing.
It's gonna be King Simba's finest fling.

Simba:
Oh, I just can't wait to be king.
Oh, I just can't wait to be king.
Oh I just can't wait to be king!

I Have Dreamed

Lyrics by Oscar Hammerstein II
Music by Richard Rodgers

from *The King & I*

I have dreamed that your arms are lovely.
I have dreamed what a joy you'll be.
I have dreamed every word you'll whisper
When you're close, close to me.

How you look in the glow of evening,
I have dreamed and enjoyed the view.
In these dreams I've loved you so
That by now I think I know
What it's like to be loved by you.
I will love being loved by you.

The Impossible Dream (The Quest)

Lyric by Joe Darion
Music by Mitch Leigh

from *Man Of La Mancha*

To dream the impossible dream,
To fight the unbeatable foe,
To bear with unbearable sorrow,
To run where the brave dare not go.

To right the unrightable wrong,
To love pure and chaste from afar,
To try when your arms are too weary,
To reach the unreachable star!

This is my quest,
To follow that star,
No matter how hopeless,
No matter how far;
To fight for the right
Without question or pause.
To be willing to march into hell for a heavenly
    cause!

And I know,
If I'll only be true
To this glorious quest,
That my heart
Will lie peaceful and calm,
When I'm laid to my rest,

And the world will be better for this;
That one man, scorned and covered with scars,
Still strove with his last ounce of courage,
To reach the unreachable stars.

I Still Believe

Music By Claude-Michel Schönberg
Lyrics by Alain Boublil & Richard Maltby Jr.
Adapted from original French Lyrics by Alain Boublil

from *Miss Saigon*

Kim:
Last night I watched him sleeping,
My body pressed to him,
And then he started speaking.
The name I heard him speak was Kim.
Yes I know that this was years ago
But when moonlight fills my room I know
You are here still.
I still, I still believe you will return.
I know you will.
My heart against all odds holds still.
Yes still, I still believe.
I know as long as I can keep believing
I'll live, I'll live,
Love cannot die.
You will return, you will return
And I alone know why.

Ellen:
Last night I watched you sleeping.
Once more the nightmare came.
I heard you cry out something,
A word that sounded like a name.
And it hurts me more than I can bear,
Knowing part of you I'll never share,
Never know.
But still, I still believe the time will come
When nothing keeps us apart.
My heart for evermore holds still.
It's all over, I'm here, there is nothing to fear.
Chris, what's haunting you?
Can't you let me inside what you so want to
  hide.
I need you too.

Ellen:
For still,

Kim:
I will hold you all night, I will make it alright.

Ellen:
I still believe,

Kim:
You are safe with me.

Ellen:
As long as I can keep believing I'll live.

Kim:
And I wish you would tell,
What you don't want to tell.
What your hell must be.

Ellen:
I'll live. You will return.
And I know why I'm yours.

Kim:
You can sleep now, you can cry now.
I'm your wife now, for life.

Both:
Until we die.

I Still Believe In Love

Words by Carole Bayer Sager
Music by Marvin Hamlisch

from *They're Playing Our Song*

After all the tears I cried,
You'd think I would give up on love,
Get off that line,
But maybe I can get it right this time.

I was there as passion turned to pain,
Sunshine turned to rainy days,
Yet here I am,
Ready to begin once again.

All my life I've been a dreamer,
Dreaming dreams that never quite come true,
But I still believe in love,
And love believin',
Maybe you can make my dreams come true.

Here, content with who I am,
I'm reachin' out my hand to him [her],
Once again,
At least I know I made myself a friend.

All my life I've been a dreamer,
Dreaming dreams that always broke in two.
But I still believe in love,
And love believin',
I'll keep on dreamin' because I still believe in
    love.
I still believe in love,
And me and you,
I still believe in love.

I Whistle A Happy Tune

Lyrics by Oscar Hammerstein II
Music by Richard Rodgers

from *The King & I*

Whenever I feel afraid
I hold my head erect
And whistle a happy tune,
So no one will suspect
I'm afraid.

While shivering in my shoes
I strike a careless pose
And whistle a happy tune,
And no one ever knows
I'm afraid.

The result of this deception
Is very strange to tell,
For when I fool the people I fear
I fool myself as well!

I whistle a happy tune,
And every single time
The happiness in the tune
Convinces me that I'm
Not afraid!

Make believe you're brave
And the trick will take you far;
You may be as brave
As you make believe you are.
You may be as brave
As you make believe you are.

I'd Be Surprisingly Good For You

Music by Andrew Lloyd Webber
Lyrics by Tim Rice

from *Evita*

Eva:
It seems crazy but you must believe
There's nothing calculated, nothing planned,
Please forgive me if I seem naïve
I would never want to force your hand.
But please understand,
I'd be good for you.

I don't always rush in like this
Twenty seconds after saying hello
Telling strangers I'm too good to miss
If I'm wrong I hope you'll tell me so:
But you really should know,
I'd be good for you.
I'd be surprisingly good for you.

I won't go on if I'm boring you.
But do you understand my point of view?
Do you like what you hear, what you see,
And would you be good for me too?

I'm not talking of a hurried night
A frantic tumble then a shy goodbye.
Creeping home before it gets too light,
That's not the reason that I caught your eye,
Which has to imply I'd be good for you
I'd be surprisingly good for you.

Peron:
Please go on, you enthrall me!
I can understand you perfectly
And I like what I hear, what I see,
And knowing me
I would be good for you too.

Eva:
I'm not talking of a hurried night
A frantic tumble then a shy goodbye
Creeping home before it gets too light,
That's not the reason that I caught your eye,
Which has to imply I'd be good for you
I'd be surprisingly good for you.

I'd Give My Life For You

Music by Claude-Michel Schönberg
Lyrics by Richard Maltby Jr. & Alain Boublil
Adapted from original French Lyrics by Alain Boublil

from *Miss Saigon*

You, who I cradled in my arms,
You, asking as little as you can.
Little snip of a little man.
I know I'd give my life for you.

You didn't ask me to be born, you.
Why should you learn of war or pain?
To make sure you're not hurt again,
I swear I'd give my life for you.

I've tasted love beyond all fear.
And you should know it's love
That brought you here.
And in one perfect night,
When the stars burned like new,
I knew what I must do.

I'll give you a million things
I'll never own,
I'll give you a world to conquer
When you're grown.

Refrain:
You will be who you want to be.
You can choose whatever heaven grants.
As long as you can have your chance,
I swear I'd give my life for you.
Sometimes I wake up reaching for him.
I feel his shadow brush my head,
But there's just moonlight on my bed.
Was he a ghost? Was he a lie?
That made my body laugh and cry?
Then by my side the proof I see:
His little one. Gods of the sun,
Bring him to me!

Refrain

No one can stop what I must do.
I swear I'll give my life for you!

I'll Never Fall In Love Again

Lyric by Hal David
Music by Burt Bacharach

from *Promises, Promises*

What do you get when you fall in love,
A girl {guy} with a pin to burst your bubble,
That's what you get for all your trouble,
I'll never fall in love again.
I'll never fall in love again.

What do you get when you kiss a girl {guy},
You get enough germs to catch pneumonia,
After you do, she'll {he'll} never phone you;
I'll never fall in love again.

Refrain:
I'll never fall in love again.
Don't tell me what it's all about,
'Cause I've been there and I'm glad I'm out;
Out of those chains, those chains that
    bind you,
That is why I'm here to remind you.
What do you get when you fall in love,
You only get lies and pain and sorrow,
So for at least until tomorrow,
I'll never fall in love again,
I'll never fall in love again.

What do you get when you give your heart,
You get it all broken up and battered,
That's what you get, a heart that's tattered;
I'll never fall in love again.

Refrain

What do you get when you need a girl {guy},
You get enough tears to fill an ocean,
That's what you get for your devotion;
I'll never fall in love again.

Refrain

I'll Know

Words & Music by Frank Loesser

from *Guys & Dolls*

Sarah:
For I've imagined ev'ry bit of him,
From his strong moral fibre,
To the wisdom in his head,
To the homey aroma of his pipe.

Sky:
You have wished yourself
A Scarsdale Galahad,
The breakfast eating,
Brooks Brothers type!

Sarah (Spoken):
Yes.

(Sung):
And I shall meet him
When the time is ripe.

I'll know when my love comes along,
I won't take a chance.
For oh, he'll be just what I need,
Not some fly-by-night Broadway romance.

Sky:
And you'll know at a glance
By the two pair of pants.

Sarah:
I'll know by the calm steady voice,
Those feet on the ground.
I'll know as I run to his arms,
That at last I've come home safe and sound.

And till then,
I shall wait,
And till then, I'll be strong.
For I'll know when my love comes along.

Sky:
Mine will come as a surprise to me,
Mine, I leave to chance,
And chemistry.

Sarah (Spoken):
Chemistry?

Sky (Spoken):
Yes, chemistry.

(Sung):
Suddenly I'll know when my love
    comes along,
I'll know then and there.
I'll know at the sight of her face
How I care, how I care, how I care!

And I'll stop,
And I'll stare.
And I'll know, long before we can speak,
I'll know in my heart,
I'll know, and I won't ever ask,
"Am I right? Am I wise? Am I smart?"
But I'll stop,
And I'll stare,
At that face in the throng,
Yes, I'll know when my love comes along.

Sarah:
I'll know.

Both:
When my love comes along

ADDITIONAL LYRICS

Sarah:
I won't take a chance,
My love will be just what I need,
Not some fly-by-night Broadway romance,
And till then,
I shall wait,
And till then, I'll be strong.
For I'll know when my love comes along.

I'll Never Say No

By Meredith Willson

from *The Unsinkable Molly Brown*

I'll never say no to you,
Whatever you say or do.
If you ask me to wait
For a lifetime,
You know I'll gladly wait
For a lifetime or two,
Just to look at you.

Refrain:
I'll smile when you say, "Be glad."
I'll weep if you want me sad.
Today is tomorrow,
If you want it so,
I'll stay or I'll go,
But I'll never say no.

Refrain

I'm Gonna Sit Right Down
And Write Myself A Letter

Words & Music by Fred E. Ahlert & Joe Young

from *Ain't Misbehavin'*

I'm gonna sit right down
And write myself a letter
And make believe it came from you.
I'm gonna write words, oh so sweet,
They're gonna knock me off my feet.
A lot of kisses on the bottom,
I'll be glad I got 'em.
I'm gonna smile and say,
"I hope you're feeling better"
And close "with love" the way you do.
I'm gonna sit right down
And write myself a letter
And make believe it came from you.

I'm Martin Guerre

Music by Claude-Michel Schönberg
Lyrics by Alain Boublil & Stephen Clark

from *Martin Guerre*

They say they follow the Lord's will,
Still they torture, still they'd kill
To make a young man reach his prime.
They say he's cursed, he's Satan's child,
I'm just a boy, betrayed, defiled,
All a young man needs is time.

Damn them all, while they run with the pack.
They will pay for the scars on my back.

They want my blood,
They're ready to feed.
They don't even know the man that they bleed.
As if a man can love on demand,
Accept his life is already planned.
There's no demon inside,
Just a man full of pride,
For my hopes haven't died.

Look…Look I'm Martin Guerre,
Too young to love but still above
The lie they live.
Yes I'm Martin Guerre,
A man who knows how evil grows
And can't afford to give.
Soon they will see
A man can choose to be free.
They all look for someone to blame
But I swear it aloud, I will be proud
That Martin Guerre is my name.

First I trusted Pierre,
I was sold at the shrine.
Then I trusted the priest,
Now my blood runs like wine.
And then there was Bertrande.
It seems all love must turn to dust,
There must be someone I can trust.

Look I'm Martin Guerre,
Father I'm brave and from your grave
You'll keep me strong.
Yes, I'm Martin Guerre,
For they will learn when I return
That I belong.
Soon you will see
That I can choose to be free.
They all look for someone to blame
But I swear it aloud, I will be proud
I'm Martin Guerre.

They all look for someone to blame
But I swear it aloud, I will be proud
That Martin Guerre is my name!

I've Grown Accustomed To Her Face

Words by Alan Jay Lerner
Music by Frederick Loewe

from *My Fair Lady*

I've grown accustomed to her face
She almost makes the day begin.
I've grown accustomed to the tune,
She whistles night and noon,
Her smiles, her frowns,
Her ups, her downs
Are second nature to me now;
Like breathing out and breathing in.
I was serenely independent
And content before we met;
Surely, I could always
Be that way again and yet,
I've grown accustomed to her looks;
Accustomed to her voice
Accustomed to her face.

I've grown accustomed to her face
She almost makes the day begin.
I've gotten used to hear her say:
"Good morning" every day,
Her joys, her woes,
Her highs, her lows
Are second nature to me now;
Like breathing out and breathing in.
I'm very grateful she's a woman
And so easy to forget
Rather like a habit
One can always break and yet,
I've grown accustomed to the trace
Of something in the air;
Accustomed to her face.

I'm Still Here

Words & Music by Stephen Sondheim

from *Follies*

Good times and bum times,
I've seen them all and, my dear,
I'm still here.
Plush velvet sometimes,
Sometimes just pretzels and beer,
But I'm here.
I've stuffed the dailies in my shoes,
Strummed ukuleles, sung the blues,
Seen all my dreams disappear,
But I'm here.

I've slept in shanties,
Guest of the W.P.A.
But I'm here.
Danced in my scanties,
Three bucks a night was the pay,
But I'm here.
I've stood on breadlines with the best,
Watched while the headlines did the rest.
In the depression was I depressed?
Nowhere near.
I met a big financier and I'm here.

I've been through Ghandi,
Windsor and Wally's affair,
And I'm here.
Amos 'n' Andy
Mahjongg and platinum hair,
And I'm here.
I got through Abie's Irish Rose,
Five Dionne babes, Major Bowes,
Had heebie jeebies for Beebe's Bathysphere.
I lived through Brenda Frazier, and I'm here.

I've gotten through Herbert and
    J. Edgar Hoover,
Gee, that was fun and a half.
When you've been through Herbert and
    J. Edgar Hoover,
Anything else is a laugh.

I've been through Reno,
I've been through Beverly Hills,
And I'm here.
Reefers and vino,
Rest cures, religion and pills,
And I'm here.
Been called a pinko Commie tool,
Got through it stinko by my pool.
I should have gone to an acting school,
That seems clear.
Still, someone said, "She's sincere,"
So I'm here.

Black sable one day,
Next day it goes into hock.
But I'm here.
Top billing Monday,
Tuesday you're touring in stock,
But I'm here.
First you're another sloe-eyed vamp,
Then someone's mother,
Then you're camp.
Then you career from career to career.

I'm almost through my memoirs
And I'm here.

I've gotten through "Hey lady aren't
    you whoozis?
Wow! What a looker you were."
Or better yet, "Sorry, I thought
    you were whoozis,
Whatever happened to her?"

Good times and bum times,
I've seen 'em all my dear,
I'm still here.
Plush velvet sometimes,
Sometimes just pretzels and beer,
But I'm here.
I've run the gamut, A to Z.
Three cheers and dammit, c'est la vie.
I got through all of last year.

And I'm here.
Lord knows, at least I was there,
And I'm here!
Look who's here!
I'm still here!

I've Never Been In Love Before

Words & Music by Frank Loesser

from *Guys & Dolls*

I've never been in love before,
Now all at once it's you.
It's you forever more.

I've never been in love before.
I thought my heart was safe,
I thought I knew the score.

But this is wine
That's all too strange and strong.
I'm full of foolish song,
And out my song must pour.
So please forgive this helpless haze I'm in.
I've really never been in love before.

If I Can't Love Her

Music by Alan Menken
Lyrics by Tim Rice

from Walt Disney's *Beauty & The Beast*

And in my twisted face,
There's not the slightest trace
Of anything that even hints of kindness.
And from my tortured shape,
No comfort, no escape.
I see, but deep within is utter blindness.
Hopeless, as my dream dies.
As the time flies, love a lost illusion.
Helpless, unforgiven.
Cold and driven to this sad conclusion.

No beauty could move me,
No goodness improve me.
No power on Earth,
If I can't love her.
No passion could reach me,
No lesson could teach me
How I could have loved her,
And make her love me too.
If I can't love her, then who?

Long ago, I should have seen
All the things I could have been.
Careless and unthinking,
I moved onward!

No pain could be deeper.
No life could be cheaper.
No point anymore,
If I can't love her.
No spirit could win me.
No hope left within me,
Hope I could have loved her,
And that she'd set me free.
But it's not to be.
If I can't love her,
Let the world be done with me.

If I Loved You

Lyrics by Oscar Hammerstein II
Music by Richard Rodgers

from *Carousel*

If I loved you,
Time and again I would try to say
All I'd want you to know.
If I loved you,
Words wouldn't come in an easy way,
'Round in circles I'd go.
Longin' to tell you, but afraid and shy,
I'd let my golden chances pass me by!
Soon you'd leave me,
Off you would go in the mist of day,
Never, never to know
How I loved you,
If I loved you.

If I Ruled The World

Words by Leslie Bricusse
Music by Cyril Ornadel

from *Pickwick*

If I ruled the world
Every day would be the first day of spring,
Every heart would have a new song to sing
And we'd sing of the joy every morning would
   bring.

If I ruled the world
Every man would be as free as a bird,
Every voice would be a voice to be heard.
Take my word we would treasure each day that
   occurred.

My world would be a beautiful place
Where we would weave such wonderful
   dreams.
My world would wear a smile on its face
Like the man in the moon has when the moon
   beams.

If I ruled the world
Every man would say the world was his friend.
There'd be happiness that no man could end.
No, my friend, not if I ruled the world.
Every head would be held up high.
There'd be sunshine in everyone's sky
If the day ever dawned when I ruled the world.

If You Could See Her

Music by John Kander
Lyrics by Fred Ebb

from *Cabaret*

I know what you're thinking,
You wonder why I chose her
Out of all the ladies in the world.
That's just a first impression,
What's a good first impression?
If you knew her like I do,
It would change your point of view.

If you could see her thru my eyes,
You wouldn't wonder at all.
If you could see her thru my eyes,
I guarantee you would fall. (like I did)
When we're in public together,
I hear society moan,
But if they could see her thru my eyes,
Maybe they'd leave us alone.

How can I speak of her virtues?
I don't know where to begin.
She's clever, she's sweet, she reads music,
She doesn't smoke or drink gin. (like I do)
Yet when we're walking together,
They sneer if I'm holding her hand,
If they could see her thru my eyes,
Maybe they'd all understand.

I understand your objection,
I grant you my problem's not small;
But if you could see her thru my eyes,
She isn't a meeskite at all. (alternative: It isn't
    peculiar at all.)

If I Were A Bell

Words & Music by Frank Loesser

from *Guys & Dolls*

Ask me how do I feel,
Ask me now that we're cozy and clinging.
Well sir, all I can say is
If I were a bell I'd be ringing.
From the moment we kissed tonight
That's the way I've just got to behave.
Boy, if I were a lamp I'd light
Or if I were a banner I'd wave.

Ask me how do I feel,
Little me with my quiet upbringing.
Well sir, all I can say is
If I were a gate I'd be swinging.
And if I were a watch I'd start popping my
    spring.
Or if I were a bell I'd go ding dong ding dong
    ding.

Ask me how do I feel
From this chemistry lesson I'm learning.
Well sir, all I can say is
If I were a bridge I'd be burning.
Yes, I knew my morale would crack
From the wonderful way you looked.
Boy, if I were a duck I'd quack
Or if I were a goose I'd be cooked.

Ask me how do I feel,
Ask me now that we're fondly caressing.
Pal, if I were a salad
I know I would be splashing my dressing.
Or if I were a season I'd surely be spring.
Or if I were a bell I'd go ding dong ding dong
    ding.

If My Friends Could See Me Now

Music by Cy Coleman
Lyrics by Dorothy Fields

from *Sweet Charity*

Tonight at eight you should a seen
A chauffeur pull up in a rented limousine!
My neighbors burned! They like to die!
When I tell them who is getting' in and goin'
    out is I!

If they could see me now, that little gang of
    mine,
I'm eating fancy chow and drinking fancy wine.
I'd like those stumble bums to see for a fact
The kind of top-drawer, first-rate chums I
    attract.
All I can say is "Wowee! Look at where I am.
Tonight I landed , pow! Right in a pot of jam."
What a set up! Holy cow!
They'd never believe it,
If My Friends Could See Me Now!

If they could see me now, my little dusty group,
Traipsin' 'round this million dollar chicken
    coop.
I'd hear those thrift shop cats say : "Brother, get
    her!
Draped on a bedspread made from three kinds
    of fur."
All I can say is "Wow! Wait till the riff and raff
See just exactly how he signed his autograph".

What a build-up! Holy Cow!
They'd never believe it,
If My Friends Could See Me Now!

If they could see me now, alone with Mister V.,
Who's waitin' on me like he was a maitre d'.
I hear my buddies saying: "Crazy, what gives?
Tonight she's living like the other half lives."
To think the highest brow, which I must say is
    he,
Should pick the lowest brow, which there's no
    doubt is me.

What a step up! Holy cow!
They'd never believe it,
If My Friends Could See Me Now!

If You Really Knew Me

Words by Carole Bayer Sager
Music by Marvin Hamlisch

from *They're Playing Our Song*

If you really knew me,
If you really, truly knew me,
Maybe you would see
The other side of me I seldom see.

If there were no music,
If your melody stopped playing,
Would he be the kind of man *(girl)*
I'd want to see tonight?

Does the man *(girl)* make the music
Or does the music make the man *(girl)*?
And am I ev'rything I thought I'd be?

If you really knew me,
If you'd take the time to understand,
Maybe you could find me,
The part I left behind me,
Maybe you'd remind me of who I am.

N.B
Female singers may substitute "he" wherever "you" appears.
Male singers may substitute "she" wherever "you" appears.

In Buddy's Eyes (Buddy's There)

Words & Music by Stephen Sondheim

from *Follies*

Life is slow but it seems exciting,
'Cause Buddy's there.
Gourmet cooking and letter writing
And knowing Buddy's there.

Ev'ry morning,
Don't faint, I tend the flowers.
Can you believe it?
Ev'ry weekend ,
I paint for umpteen hours.
And yes, I miss a lot,
Living like a shut-in.
No, I haven't got
Cooks and cars and diamonds.
Yes, my clothes are not
Paris fashions, but in
Buddy's eyes,
I'm young, I'm beautiful.
In Buddy's eyes,
I don't get older.
So life is ducky and time goes flying,
And I'm so lucky I feel like crying and…

In Buddy's eyes,
I'm young, I'm beautiful,
In Buddy's eyes,
I can't get older.
I'm still the princess,
Still the prize.

In Buddy's eyes,
I'm young, I'm beautiful.
In Buddy's arms,
On Buddy's shoulder,
I won't get older.
Nothing dies.

And all I ever dreamed I'd be,
The best I ever thought of me,
Is ev'ry minute there to see,
In Buddy's eyes.

In My Own Little Corner

Lyrics by Oscar Hammerstein II
Music by Richard Rodgers

from *Cinderella*

I'm as mild and meek as a mouse,
When I hear a command I obey.
But I know of a spot in my house
Where no one can stand in my way.

In my own little corner, in my own little chair,
I can be whatever I want to be.
On the wing of my fancy I can fly anywhere
And the world will open its arms to me.

I'm a young Norwegian princess or a milkmaid,
I'm the greatest prima donna in Milan,
I'm an heiress who has always had her silk
    made
By her own flock of silkworms in Japan!

I'm a girl men go mad for,
Love's a game I can play
With a cool and confident kind of air,
Just as long as I stay in my own little corner,
All alone in my own little chair.

I can be whatever I want to be.
I'm a slave in Calcutta,
I'm a queen in Peru,
I'm a mermaid dancing upon the sea.

I'm a huntress on an African safari
(It's a dang'rous type of sport and yet it's fun;)
In the night I sally forth to seek my quarry,
And I find I forgot to bring my gun!

I am lost in the jungle
All alone and unarmed
When I meet a lioness in her lair!
Then I'm glad to be back in my own little
    corner,
All alone in my own little chair.

It Might As Well Be Spring

Lyrics by Oscar Hammerstein II
Music by Richard Rodgers

from *State Fair*

I'm as restless as a willow in a windstorm.
I'm as jumpy as a puppet on a string!
I'd say that I had spring fever,
But I know it isn't spring.
I am starry-eyed and vaguely discontented,
Like a nightingale without a song to sing.
Oh, why should I have spring fever
When it isn't even spring?

I keep wishing I were somewhere else,
Walking down a strange new street,
Hearing words that I have never heard
From a man I've yet to meet.

I'm as busy as a spider, spinning daydreams,
I'm as giddy as a baby on a swing.
I haven't seen a crocus or a rosebud
Or a robin on the wing,
But I feel so gay, in a melancholy way,
That it might as well be spring,
It might as well be spring.

It's A Grand Night For Singing

Lyrics by Oscar Hammerstein II
Music by Richard Rodgers

from *State Fair*

It's a grand night for singing,
The moon is flying high,
And somewhere a bird who is bound he'll be
    heard,
Is throwing his heart at the sky.
It's a grand night for singing,
The stars are bright above,
The earth is aglow, and, to add to the show,
I think I am falling in love,
Falling, falling in love.

It's The Hard-Knock Life

Lyric by Martin Charnin
Music by Charles Strouse

from *Annie*

It's a hard-knock life for us!
It's a hard-knock life for us!
'Stead-a treated we got tricked.
'Stead-a kisses we got kicked.
It's the hard-knock life!

Got no folks to speak of, so,
It's the hard-knock row we hoe,
Cotton blankets 'stead-a wool,
Empty bellies 'stead-a full,
It's the hard-knock life.

Don't it feel like this wind is always howlin'?
Don't it seem like there's never any light?
Once a day don't you want to throw the towel
    in?
It's easier than puttin' up a fight.

No one's there when your dreams at night get
    creepy,
No one cares if you grow or if you shrink,
No one cries when your eyes get red and weepy.
From the cryin' you would think this place
    would sink.

Oh!

Empty belly life!
Rotten smelly life!
Full of sorrow life!
No tomorrow life!

Santa Claus we never see,
Santa Claus, what's that? Who's he?
No one cares for you a smidge,
When you're in an orphanage!
It's a hard knock life.

Yank the whiskers from her chin.
Jab her with a safety pin.
Make her drink a Mickey Finn.
I love you, Miss Hannigan.

It's the hard-knock life for us.
It's the hard-knock life for us.
No one cares for you a smidge,
When you're in an orphanage!
It's the hard knock life.

The Joint Is Jumpin'

Words by Andy Razaf & J.C. Johnson
Music by Thomas "Fats" Waller

from *Ain't Misbehavin'*

They have a new expression along old Harlem
way,
That tells you when a party is ten times more
than gay.
To say that things are jumpin' leaves not a
single doubt,
That everything is in full swing when you hear a
body shout:
Spoken: (Here 'tis)

The joint is jumpin',
It's really jumpin'.
Come in cats an' check your hats,
I mean this joint is jumpin'.

The piano's thumpin',
The dancers bumpin'.
This here spot is more than hot,
In fact the joint is jumpin'.

Check your weapons at the door,
Be sure to pay your quarter.
Burn your leather on the floor,
Grab anybody's daughter.

The roof is rockin',
The neighbor's knockin'.
We're all bums when the wagon comes.
I mean this joint is jumpin'.
Spoken: (Let it beat!)

The joint is jumpin',
It's really jumpin'.
Every Mose is on his toes,
I mean the joint is jumpin'.

No time for talkin',
It's time for walkin'. (Yes!)
Grab a jug and cut the rug,
I mean this joint is jumpin'.

Get your pig feet, beer and gin,
There's plenty in the kitchen.
Who is that that just came in?
Just look at the way he's switchin'.

Don't mind the hour,
'Cause I'm in power.
I got bail if we go to jail.
I mean the joint is jumpin'.

The joint is jumpin',
It's really jumpin'.
We're all bums when the wagon comes,
I mean this joint is jumpin'.

Spoken:
(Don't give your right name. No, No, No!)

The Journey Home

Music By A. R. Rahman
Lyrics By Don Black

from *Bombay Dreams*

The journey home is never too long;
Your heart arrives before the train.
The journey home is never too long;
Some yesterdays always remain.

I'm going back to when my heart was light,
When my pillow was a ship I sailed through the
    night.

The journey home is never too long
When open arms are waiting there.
The journey home is never too long
There's room to love and room to spare.

I want to feel the way that I did then.
I'll think my wishes through before I wish
    again.

Not every road you come across
Is one you have to take.
No, sometimes standing still can be
The best move you ever could make.

The journey home is never too long
Home helps to heal the deepest pain.
The journey home is never too long
Your hearts arrives before the train.

June Is Bustin' Out All Over

Lyrics by Oscar Hammerstein II
Music by Richard Rodgers

from *Carousel*

March went out like a lion,
A-whippin' up the water in the bay.
Then April cried
And stepped aside,
And along come pretty little May!

May was full of promises,
But she didn't keep 'em quick enough fer
    some,
And a crowd of Doubtin' Thomases
Was predictin' that the summer'd never come.

But it's comin', by gum!
Y' ken feel it come,
Y' ken feel it in yer heart,
Y' ken see it in the ground,
Y' ken see it in the trees,
Y' ken hear it in the breeze—
Look around, look around, look around!

June is bustin' out all over!
All over the meadow and the hill,
Buds're bustin' outa bushes,
And the rompin' river pushes
Ev'ry little wheel that wheels beside a mill.
June is bustin' out all over!
The feelin' is gettin' so intense
That the young Virginia creepers
Hev been huggin' the bejeepers
Outa all the mornin' glories on the fence.
Because it's June!
June, June, June,
Because it's June!
June, June, June,
Jest because it's June, June, June!

Fresh and alive and gay and young,
June is a love song sweetly sung.

June is bustin' out all over!
The saplin's are bustin' out with sap!
Love hes found my brother, "Junior,"
And my sister's even lunier,
And my ma is gettin' kittenish with Pap.
June is bustin' out all over!
To ladies the men are payin' court.
Lotsa ships are kept at anchor
Jest because the captains hanker
Fer a comfort they ken only get in port!
Because it's June!
June, June, June.
Jest because it's June, June, June!

June makes the bay look bright and new,
Sails gleamin' white on sunlit blue.

June is bustin' out all over!
The ocean is full of Jacks and Jills.
With her little tail a-swishin'
Ev'ry lady fish is wishin'
That a male would come and grab her by
    the gills!
June is bustin' out all over!
The sheep aren't sleepin' any more.
All the rams that chase the ewe sheep
Are determined there'll be new
sheep,
And the ewe sheep aren't even keepin' score!
On accounta it's June!
June, June, June,
Jest because it's June, June, June!

Just A Housewife

Words & Music by Craig Carnelia

from *Working*

All I am is just a housewife.
Nothing special, nothing great.
What I do is kinda boring.
If you'd rather, it can wait.

All I am is someone's mother.
All I am is someone's wife.
All of which seems unimportant.
All it is is just my life.

Do the laundry, wash the dishes.
Take the dog out, clean the house.
Shop for groc'ries, look for specials.
God, it sounds so Mickey Mouse.

Drop the kids off,
Pick the shirts up.
Try to lose weight,
Try again.
Keep the troops fed,
Pick their things up.
Lose your patience,
Count to ten.
(Spoken) Two, three, four, five, six,
Seven, eight, nine, ten.
Four, five, six, seven, eight, nine...

All I am is just a housewife.
Just a housewife, nothing great.
What I do is out of fashion.
What I feel is out of date.

All I am is someone's mother.
Right away I'm "not too bright."
What I do is "unfulfilling."
So the T.V. talk shows tell me ev'ry night.

I don't mean to complain and all,
But they make you feel
Like you're two feet tall,
When you're just a wife.

Nowadays all the magazines
Make a bunch o' beans
Out o' fam'ly life.
You're a wiz if you go to work,
But you're just a jerk
If you say you won't.
Women's Lib says they think it's fine
If the choice is mine,
But you know they don't!

What I do, what I choose to do,
May be dumb to you,
But it's not to me.
Is it dumb that they need me there?
Is it dumb to care?

'Cause I do, you see.
And I mean, did ya ever think,
Really stop and think
What a job it was,
Doing all the things
That a housewife does?

I'm afraid it's unimpressive.
All I am is someone's mother,
Nothing special,
What I do is unexciting,
Kinda dull.
Take the kids here,
Take the kids there.
I don't mean to complain and all.

All I am is busy, busy.
All I am is like my mother.
All I am is just a housewife.

Justice Will Be Done

Music by Claude-Michel Schönberg
Lyrics by Alain Boublil & Stephen Clark

from *Martin Guerre*

Think of all our fathers
Fighting for these lands.
Think of all your children,
Their future in our hands.

Shall they'll all be poisoned?
Will you tell them why?
Have we lost our courage?
Will we let them die?

Stand up for your homeland,
Proud beneath the sun.
In the heat of battle,
Justice will be done.

All that you have loved here;
Remember what you're worth.
All that you have worked for;
Grown within this earth.

Fields where you have laboured,
Soon they'll be defiled.
Plagues of sin will spread through
The blood of ev'ry child.

Come the day of glory,
Fight until we've won.
If you love your country,
Justice will be done.

It is here, by your hands
That the future is made.
We must claim what is ours
By the stroke of the blade.

They will die for their treason,
They will die for their shame.
They will die by the sword,
They will die by the flame!

Bring them to the streets now,
Soon they'll run with blood.
Then we'll see they have no souls,
Red rivers bursting, see them flood.

Feel the touch of evil, this is how it starts.
Satan's here within us fighting for our hearts.
Let us join together, stand up one by one.
In the name of Jesus justice will be done!

Kate The Great

Words & Music by Cole Porter

from *Anything Goes*

Katherine of Russia, that potentate,
Knew that her job was to fascinate.
Some people called her a reprobate,
But still she's known as Kate the Great.
To sessions of congress she wouldn't go,
Never heckled the crowd on the radio.
She never would mix in affairs of state,
But in affairs of the heart, how Kate was great!

As few lovely ladies today,
She knew where a woman should stay.
She never laid a five-year plan,
But was there ever such a girl,
At laying a plan
For a man?
So drink to that jovial jade
And think of the hist'ry she made.

Why, she made the congress,
She made the premier,
She made the clergy,
And she made 'em cheer.
She made the butler,
She made the groom,
She made the maid,
Who made the room.

She made the army,
She made the marines,
Made some of them princes,
And some of them queens.
And when she was still discontent,
Kate'd create a new regiment.

So, beautiful ladies, before too late,
Follow the lead of this potentate,
Give up arranging affairs of state,
And stay in the hay like Kate the Great,
Hay-de-hay!
Hay-de-hay!
Hay-de-hay!
Hay-de-hay!
So stay in the hay like Kate the Great!

King Herod's Song

Music by Andrew Lloyd Webber
Lyrics by Tim Rice

from *Jesus Christ Superstar*

Jesus, I am overjoyed to meet you face to face,
You've been getting quite a name all around the
place.
Healing cripples, raising from the dead,
And now I understand you're God; at least that's
what you've said.

So, you are the Christ, you're the great Jesus
Christ!
Prove to me that you're divine,
Change my water into wine.
That's all you need to do,
And I'll know it's all true,
C'mon King of the Jews.

Jesus, you just won't believe the hit you've made
'round here,
You are all we talk about, the wonder of the
year.
Oh what a pity if it's all a lie,
Still I'm sure that you can rock the cynics if you
try.

So, you are the Christ you're the great Jesus
Christ!
Prove to me that you're no fool,
Walk across my swimming pool.
If you do that for me
Then I'll let you go free,
C'mon King of the Jews.

I only ask things I'd ask any superstar.
What is it that you have got that puts you where
you are?
I am waiting, yes I'm a captive fan,
I'm dying to be shown that you're not just any
man.

So, if you are Christ, yes the great Jesus Christ,
Feed my household with this bread,
You can do it on your head.
Or has something gone wrong?
Why do you take so long?
C'mon King of the Jews.

Hey! Aren't you scared of me Christ?
Mister Wonderful Christ!
You're a joke you're no the Lord
You're nothing but a fraud
Take him away he's got nothing to say!

Get out you King of the,
Get out,
Get out you King of the Jews!
Get out you King of the Jews!

Get out of my life!

The Ladies Who Lunch

Music & Lyrics by Stephen Sondheim
from *Company*

Here's to the ladies who lunch—
Everybody laugh.
Lounging in their caftans and planning a
 brunch
On their own behalf.
Off to the gym
Then to a fitting
Claiming they're fat.
And looking grim
'Cause they've been sitting choosing a hat.

Spoken:
Does anyone still wear a hat?

I'll drink to that.

Here's to the girls who stay smart.
Aren't they a gas?
Rushing to their classes in optical art,
Wishing it would pass.
Another long, exhausting day,
Another thousand dollars.
A matinee:
A Pinter play,
Perhaps a piece of Mahler's.
I'll drink to that,
And one for Mahler.

Here's to the girls who play wife.
Aren't they too much?
Keeping house, but clutching a copy of Life—
Just to keep in touch.
The ones who follow the rules
And meet themselves at the schools—
Too busy to know that they're fools.
Aren't they a gem?

I'll drink to them!
Let's all drink to them!

Here's to the girls who just watch.
Aren't they the best?
When they get depressed,
 it's a bottle of Scotch,
Plus a little jest.
Another chance to disapprove,
Another brilliant zinger.
Another reason not to move,
Another vodka stinger.

Scream:
Aaah…

I'll drink to that.

So here's to the girls on the go,
Everybody tries.
Look into their eyes and you'll
 see what they know:
Everybody dies.
A toast to that invincible bunch,
The dinosaurs surviving the crunch,
Let's hear it for the ladies who lunch:
Everybody rise!
Rise! Rise!
Rise! Rise!
Rise! Rise!
Rise!

The Lady Is A Tramp

Words by Lorenz Hart
Music by Richard Rodgers

from *Babes In Arms*

I've wined and dined on Mulligan stew
And never wished for turkey
As I hitched and hiked and grifted too,
From Maine to Albuquerque.
Alas, I missed the Beaux Arts Ball,
And what is twice as sad,
I was never at a party
Where they honored Noël Ca'ad.
But social circles spin too fast for me.
My hobohemia is the place for me

I get too hungry for dinner at eight.
I like the theatre, but never come late.
I never bother with people I hate.
That's why the lady is a tramp.
I don't like crap games with barons
    and earls.
Won't go to Harlem in ermine
    and pearls.
Won't dish the dirt with the
    rest of the girls.
That's why the lady is a tramp.

I like the free, fresh wind in my hair,
Life without care.
I'm broke—it's oke.
Hate California—it's cold and damp.
That's why the lady is a tramp.

I go to Coney—the beach is divine.
I go to ball games—the bleachers are fine.
I follow Winchell and read every line.
That's why the lady is a tramp.
I like a prizefight that isn't a fake.
I love the rowing on Central Park Lake.
I go to operas and stay wide awake.
That's why the lady is a tramp.
I like the green grass under my shoes.
What can I lose?
I'm flat! That's that!
I'm all alone when I lower my lamp.
That's why the lady is a tramp.

Don't know the reason for cocktails at five.
I don't like flying—I'm glad I'm alive.
I crave affection, but not when I drive.
That's why the lady is a tramp.
Folks go to London and leave me behind.

I missed the crowning, Queen Mary won't
  mind.
I don't play Scarlett in Gone with the Wind.
That's why the lady is a tramp.
I like to hang my hat where I please.
Sail with the breeze.
No dough—heigh-ho!
I love La Guardia and think he's a champ.
That's why the lady is a tramp.

Girls get massages, they cry and they moan.
Tell Lizzie Arden to leave me alone.
I'm not too hot, but my shape is my own.
That's why the lady is a tramp!
The food at Sardi's is perfect, no doubt.

I wouldn't know what the Ritz is about.
I drop a nickel and coffee comes out.
That's why the lady is a tramp!
I like the sweet, fresh rain in my face.
Diamonds and lace,
No got—so what?
For Robert Taylor I whistle and stamp.
That's why the lady is a tramp!

The Last Night Of The World

Music by Claude-Michel Schönberg
Lyrics by Richard Maltby Jr. & Alain Boublil
Adapted from original French Lyrics by Alain Boublil

from *Miss Saigon*

Chris:
In a place that won't let us feel,
In a life where nothing seems real
I have found you,
I have found you.

Kim:
In a world that's moving too fast,
In a world where nothing can last,
I will hold you,
I will hold you.

Chris:
Our lives will change when tomorrow comes.
Kim:
Tonight our hearts dream the distant drums.
Chris:
And we have music alright tearing the night.
A song played on a solo saxophone.
A crazy sound, a lonely sound,

Both:
A cry that tells me love goes on and on.
Played on a solo saxophone,
It's telling me to hold you tight,
And dance like it's the last night of the world.

Chris:
On the other side of the earth,
There's a place where life still has worth.
I will take you.

Kim:
I'll go with you.
Chris:
You won't believe all the things you'll see.
I know 'cause you'll see them all with me.

Both:
If we're together, well then,
We'll hear it again,
A song played on a solo saxophone.
A crazy sound, a lonely sound.
A cry that tells us love goes on and on.
Played on a solo saxophone.
It's telling me to hold you tight
And dance like it's the last night of the world.

Kim:
Dreams were all I ever knew.
Chris:
Dreams you won't need when I'm through.
Both:
Anywhere we may be I will sing with you our
    song.
So stay with me and hold me tight
And dance like it's the last night of the world.

Lay All Your Love On Me

Words & Music by Benny Andersson & Björn Ulvaeus

from *Mamma Mia!*

Sky:
I wasn't jealous before we met
Now every man that I see is a potential threat.
And I'm possessive, it isn't nice,
You've heard me saying that smoking is my only
  vice.
But now it isn't true,
Now everything is new,
And all I've learned
Has overturned,
I beg of you.

Sophie:
Don't go wasting your emotion
Lay all your love on me

It was like shooting a sitting duck
A little small-talk, a smile and baby, I was stuck.
I still don't know what you've done with me,
A grown-up woman should never fall so easily.
I feel a kind of fear
When I don't have you near
Unsatisfied
I skip my pride
I beg you dear.

Sky:
Don't go wasting your emotion
Lay all your love on me.

Boys:
Don't go sharing your devotion
Lay all your love on me.

Sophie:
I've had a few little love affairs.
They didn't last very long and they've been
  pretty scarce.

Sky:
I used to think that was sensible.
It makes the truth even more
  incomprehensible.

Sophie:
'Cause everything is new
And everything is you
And all I've learned
Has overturned
What can I do?

Sky/Pepper/Eddie/Boys:
Don't go wasting your emotion
Lay all your love on me.
Don't go sharing your devotion
Lay all your love on me.

Girls:
Don't go wasting your emotion
Lay all your love on me
Don't go sharing your devotion
Lay all your love on me…

Lazy Afternoon

Words & Music by John Latouche & Jerome Moross

from *The Golden Apple*

It's a lazy afternoon
And the beetle bugs are zoomin'
And the tulip trees are bloomin'
And there's not another human
In view
But us two.
It's a lazy afternoon
And the farmer leaves his reapin',
In the meadow cows are sleepin'
And the speckled trout stop leapin' upstream
As we dream.

A fat pink cloud hangs over the hill,
Unfoldin' like a rose.
If you hold my hand and sit real still
You can hear the grass as it grows.
It's a hazy afternoon
And I know a place that's quiet
'Cept for daisies running riot
And there's no one passing by it to see.
Come spend this lazy afternoon with me.

Leaning On A Lamp Post

By Noel Gay

from *Me & My Girl*

Leaning on a lamp,
Maybe you think I look a tramp,
Or you may think I'm hanging 'round to steal a
     car.
But no, I'm not a crook,
And if you think that's what I look,
I'll tell you why I'm here and what my motives
     are.

I'm leaning on a lamp-post
At the corner of the street,
In case a certain lady comes by.
Oh me,
Oh my.
I hope the little lady comes by.

I don't know if she'll get away,
She doesn't always get away,
But anyway I know that she'll try.
Oh me,
Oh my,
I hope the little lady comes by.

Refrain:
There's no other girl I could wait for,
But this one I'd break any date for,
I won't have to ask what she's late for,
She wouldn't leave me flat,
She's not a girl like that.
She's absolutely wonderful and marvelous and
     beautiful,
And anyone can understand why
I'm leaning on a lamp-post at the corner of the
     street,
In case a certain little lady comes by.

Refrain

Let Me Entertain You

Words by Stephen Sondheim
Music by Jule Styne

from *Gypsy*

Let me entertain you.
Let me make you smile.
Let me do a few tricks,
Some old and then some new tricks,
I'm very versatile.

And if you're real good,
I'll make you feel good.
I want your spirits to climb.
So let me entertain you,
And we'll have a real good time,
Yes, sir!
We'll have a real good time.

Let me entertain you,
And we'll have a real good time,
Yes, sir!
We'll have a real good time.

Let me do a few tricks,
Some old and then some new tricks.

And if you're real good,
I'll make you feel good.
I want your spirits to climb.
Let me entertain you,
And we'll have a real good time,
Yes, sir!
We'll have a real good time.

A Little Fall Of Rain

Music by Claude-Michel Schönberg
Original Lyrics by Alain Boublil & Jean-Marc Natel
English Lyrics by Herbert Kretzmer

from *Les Misérables*

Eponine:
Don't you fret, M'sieur Marius,
I don't feel any pain.
A little fall of rain
Can hardly hurt me now.
You're here, that's all I need to know.
And you will keep me safe,
And you will keep me close.
And rain will make the flowers grow.

Marius:
But you will live, 'Ponine,
Dear God above.
If I could close your wounds
With words of love.
Eponine:
Just hold me now and let it be.
Shelter me, comfort me.
Marius:
You would live a hundred years,
If I could show you how.
I won't desert you now.

Eponine:
The rain can't hurt me now.
This rain will wash away what's past.
And you will keep me safe.
And you will keep me close.
I'll sleep in your embrace at last.

The rain that brings you here
Is heaven blessed.
The skies begin to clear,
And I'm at rest.
A breath away from where you are,
I've come home from so far.
So don't you fret, M'sieur Marius,
I don't feel any pain.
A little fall of rain
Can hardly hurt me now.

Marius:
I'm here.

Eponine:
That's all I need to know.
And you will keep me safe.
And you will keep me close.
And rain will make the flowers...

Marius:
Grow.

Losing My Mind

Words & Music by Stephen Sondheim

from *Follies*

The sun comes up,
I think about you.
The coffee cup,
I think about you.
I want you so,
It's like I'm losing my mind.

The morning ends,
I think about you.
I talk to friends,
I think about you.
And do they know?
It's like I'm losing my mind.

Refrain:
All afternoon,
Doing every little chore.
The thought of you stays bright.
Sometimes I stand in the middle of the floor,
Not going left,
Not going right.
I dim the lights
And think about you,
Spend sleepless nights
To think about you.
You said you loved me,
Or were you just being kind?
Or am I losing my mind?

I want you so,
It's like I'm losing my mind.
Does no one know?
It's like I'm losing my mind.

Refrain

Love Changes Everything

Music by Andrew Lloyd Webber
Lyrics by Don Black & Charles Hart

from *Aspects of Love*

Love, love changes everything,
Hands and faces, earth and sky.
Love, love changes everything,
How you live and how you die.

Love can make the summer fly,
Or a night seem like a lifetime.

Yes love, love changes everything,
Now I tremble at your name.
Nothing in the world
Will ever be the same.

Love, love changes everything,
Days are longer, words mean more.
Love, love changes everything,
Pain is deeper than before.

Love will turn your world around,
And that world will last forever.

Yes love, love changes everything,
Brings you glory, brings you shame.
Nothing in the world
Will ever be the same.

Off into the world we go,
Planning futures, shaping years.
Love bursts in, and suddenly,
All our wisdom disappears.

Love makes fools of everyone,
All the rules we make are broken.

Yes love, love changes everyone.
Live or perish in its flame.
Love will never, never let you
Be the same.
Love will never, never let you
Be the same.

Love's Never Easy

Music By A.R. Rahman
Lyrics By Don Black

from *Bombay Dreams*

Love's never easy,
Take it from a girl who knows.
Love comes as quickly as it goes.

Love's never easy
Always moments of despair;
And we girls get more than our share.

All women want in life
Is to find a man
Who's kind and true.
We have seen life through men's eyes
So we know what pleases you.

Oh.

Love's never easy,
You will learn this lesson too.
I'll be here for you when you do.

Love's never easy,
One day soon the dream will start.
Well, that is what I tell my heart.

All women want in life
Is to find a man
Who's kind and true.
We have seen life through men's eyes
So we know what pleases you.

Oh.

Love's never easy,
Take it from a girl who knows.
Love comes as quickly as it goes.

Love's never easy,
One day soon the dream will start.
Well, that is what I tell my heart.

Oh.

Lover, Come Back to Me

Lyrics by Oscar Hammerstein II
Music by Sigmund Romberg

from *The New Moon*

You went away, I let you,
We broke the ties that bind;
I wanted to forget you
And leave the past behind.
Still, the magic of the night I met you
Seems to stay forever in my mind.

The sky was blue
And high above
The moon was new
And so was love.
This eager heart of mine was singing:
"Lover, where can you be?"

You came at last,
Love had its day,
That day is past,
You've gone away.
This aching heart of mine is singing:
"Lover, come back to me!"

When I remember every little thing you used to
do,
I'm so lonely,
Every road I walk along I've walked along with
you,
No wonder I am lonely.

The sky is blue,
The night is cold,
The moon is new,
But love is old,
And, while I'm waiting here,
This heart of mine is singing:
"Lover, come back to me!"

Mad About The Boy

Words & Music by Noel Coward

from *Words & Music*

I met him at a party just a couple of
  years ago,
He was rather over hearty and ridiculous,
But as I'd seen him on the screen,
He cast a certain spell.

I bask'd in his attraction for a couple of hours
  or so,
His manners were a fraction
  too meticulous.
If he was real or not I couldn't tell,
But like a silly fool I fell.

Mad about the boy,
I know it's stupid to be mad about the boy,
I'm so ashamed of it,
But must admit
The sleepless nights I've had about the boy.

On the silver screen,
He melts my foolish heart in ev'ry
  single scene,
Although I'm quite aware
That here and there
Are traces of the cad about the boy.

Lord knows I'm not a fool girl,
I really shouldn't care.
Lord knows I'm not a school girl,
In the flurry of her first affair.

Will it every cloy?
This odd diversity of misery and joy,
I'm feeling quite insane
And young again,
And all because I'm mad about the boy.

Will it every cloy?
This odd diversity of misery and joy,
I'm feeling quite insane
And young again,
And all because I'm mad about the boy.

It seems a little silly
For a girl of my age and weight
To walk down Piccadilly
In a haze of love,
It ought to take a good deal more
To get a bad girl down.

I should have been exempt,
For my particular kind of fate
Has taught me such contempt
For ev'ry phase of love,
And now I've been and spent
My last half-crown,
To weep about a painted clown.

Mad about the boy,
It's pretty funny, but I'm mad about the boy.
He has a gay appeal
That makes me feel
There's maybe something sad about the boy.

Walking down the street,
His eyes look out at me from people
    that I meet,
I can't believe it's true,
But when I'm blue,
In some strange way I'm glad about the boy.

I'm hardly sentimental,
Love isn't so sublime,
I have to pay my rental
And I can't afford to waste much time.

If I could employ

A little magic that would finally destroy
This dream that pains me
And enchains me,
But I can't, because I'm mad about the boy.

Mamma Mia!

Words & Music by Benny Andersson, Bjorn Ulvaeus & Stig Anderson
from *Mamma Mia!*

Donna:
I was cheated by you,
And I think you know when.
So I made up my mind
It must come to an end.

Look at me now,
Will I ever learn?
I don't know how,
But I suddenly lose control.
There's a fire within my soul.
Just one look and I can hear a bell ring.
One more look and I forget everything.

Woh,
Mamma Mia! Here I go again,
My, my, how can I resist you?
Mamma Mia! Does it show again?
My, my, just how much I missed you?

Yes, I've been broken hearted,
Blue since the day we parted.
Why, why did I ever let you go?
Mamma Mia! Now I really know
My, my, I should not have let you go.

I was angry and sad
When I knew we were through.
I can't count all the times
I have cried over you.

Look at me now,
Will I ever learn?
I don't know how,
But I suddenly lose control.
There's a fire within my soul.

Just one look and I can hear a bell ring.
One more look and I forget everything.

Woh,
Mamma Mia! Here I go again,
My, my, how can I resist you?
Mamma Mia! Does it show again?
My, my, just how much I missed you?

Yes, I've been broken hearted,
Blue since the day we parted.
Why, why did I ever let you go?
Mamma Mia! Now I really know
My, my, I should not have let you go.

Donna (Spoken):
What the hell are you doing here?
Well, I'd love to stop and chat, but I have to go
    and clean out my handbag or something.

Bill (Spoken):
Age does not wither her.

Harry (Spoken):
I was expecting a rather stout matron.

Sam (Spoken):
No, she's still Donna.

Donna/Sam/Bill/Harry (Sung):
Just one look and I can hear a bell ring.
One more look and I forget everything.

Woh,
Mamma Mia! Here I go again,
My, my, how can I resist you?
Mamma Mia! Does it show again?
My, my, just how much I missed you?

Yes, I've been broken hearted,
Ooh, since the day we parted.
Why, why did I ever let you go?
Mamma Mia! Now I really know
My, my, I should not have let you go.

Manhattan

Words by Lorenz Hart
Music by Richard Rodgers

from *The Garrick Gaieties*

Verse:
Summer journeys to Niagara
And to other places aggra-
Vate all our cares.
We'll save our fares!
I've a cozy little flat in
What is known as Manhattan,
We'll settle down
Right here in town!

Refrain:
We'll have Manhattan
The Bronx and Staten Island too.
It's lovely going through the zoo.
It's very fancy
On old Delancey Street, you know.
The subway charms us so
When balmy breezes blow
To and fro.
And tell me what street
Compares with Mott Street in July?
Sweet pushcarts gently gliding by.
The great big city's a wondrous toy
Just made for a girl and boy.
We'll turn Manhattan
Into an isle of joy.

We'll go to Greenwich,
Where modern men itch to be free;
And Bowling Green you'll see with me.
We'll bathe at Brighton;
The fish you'll frighten when you're in,
Your bathing suit so thin
Will make the shellfish grin
Fin to fin.
I'd like to take a
Sail on Jamaica Bay with you.
And fair Canarsie's Lake we'll view.
The city's bustle cannot destroy
The dreams of a girl and boy.
We'll turn Manhattan
Into an isle of joy.

We'll go to Yonkers
Where true love conquers in the wilds.
And starve together, dear, in Childs.
We'll go to Coney
And eat baloney on a roll.
In Central Park we'll stroll
Where our first kiss we stole,
Soul to soul.
Our future babies
We'll take to Abie's Irish Rose.
I hope they'll live to see it close.
The city's clamor can never spoil
The dreams of a boy and goil.
We'll turn Manhattan
Into an isle of joy.

We'll have Manhattan,
The Bronx and Staten Island too.
We'll try to cross Fifth Avenue.
As black as onyx
We'll find the Bronnix Park Express.
Our Flatbush flat, I guess,
Will be a great success,
More or less.
A short vacation
On Inspiration Point we'll spend,
And in the station house we'll end.
But Civic Virtue cannot destroy
The dreams of a girl and boy.
We'll turn Manhattan
Into an isle of joy.

Luck Be A Lady

Words & Music by Frank Loesser

from *Guys & Dolls*

They call you Lady Luck,
But there is room for doubt;
At times you have a very unladylike way of
    running out.
You're on a date with me,
The pickings have been lush,
And yet before this evening is over,
You might give me the brush.
You might forget your manners,
You might refuse to stay,
And so the best that I can do is pray.

Luck be a lady tonight.
Luck be a lady tonight.
Luck, if you've ever been a lady to begin with,
Luck be a lady tonight.

Luck, let a gentleman see,
How nice a dame you can be.
I know the way you've treated other guys you've
    been with,
Luck be a lady with me.

A lady doesn't leave her escort;
It isn't fair,
It isn't nice!
A lady doesn't wander all over the room
And blow on some other guy's dice.

So, let's keep the party polite,
Never get out of my sight.
Stick with me baby I'm the fellow you came in
    with.
Luck be a lady, luck be a lady,
Luck be a lady tonight.

Marian The Librarian

Words & Music by Meredith Willson

from *The Music Man*

Marian,
Madam librarian.

What can I do, my dear,
To catch your ear?
I love you madly, madly,
Madam librarian, Marian.
Heaven help us,
If the library caught on fire,
And the volunteer hose brigade men
Had to whisper the news to Marian,
Madam librarian.

What can I say, my dear,
To make it clear?
I need you badly, badly,
Madam librarian, Marian.
If I stumbled,
And I busted my what-you-ma-call-it,
I could lie on your floor unnoticed,
'Til my body had turned to carrion,
Madam librarian.

Now in the moonlight,
A man could sing it,
In the moonlight.
And a fellow would know that his darling
Had heard ev'ry word of his song,
With the moonlight
Helping along.

But when I try, in here,
To tell you, dear,
I love you madly, madly,
Madam librarian, Marian,
It's a long lost cause I can never win,
For the civilized world accepts
As unforgivable sin
Any talking out loud with any librarian,
Such as Marian,
Madam librarian.

Master Of The House

Music by Claude-Michel Schönberg
Original Lyrics by Alain Boublil & Jean-Marc Natel
English Lyrics by Herbert Kretzmer

from *Les Misérables*

Thernardier:
Welcome, M'sieur.
Sit yourself down,
And meet the best innkeeper in town.
As for the rest,
All of them crooks,
Rooking the guests and cooking the books.
Seldom do you see
Honest men like me.
A gent of good intent
Who's content to be:

Master of the house,
Doling out the charm,
Ready with a handshake and an open palm.
Tells a saucy tale,
Makes a little stir,
Customers appreciate a bon viveur.
Glad to do a friend a favor,
Doesn't cost me to be nice,
But nothing gets you nothing,
Ev'rything has got a little price.

Master of the house,
Keeper of the zoo,
Ready to relieve them of a sou or two.
Watering the wine,
Making up the weight,
Picking up their knickknacks
When they can't see straight.

Ev'rybody loves a landlord.
Ev'rybody's bosom friend.
I do whatever pleases,
Jesus, don't I bleed 'em in the end!
How it all increases,
All them bits and pieces,
Jesus, it's amazing how it grows!

Refrain:
Master of the house,
Quick to catch your eye,
Never wants a passerby to pass him by.
Servant to the poor,
Butler to the great,
Comforter, philosopher and lifelong mate.
Ev'rybody's boon companion,
Ev'rybody's chaperone,
Thernardier:
But lock up your valises,
Jesus, won't I skin you to the bone!

Enter, M'sieur,
Lay down your load,
Unlace your boots and rest from the road.
This weighs a ton.
Travel's a curse.
Here the goose is cooked.
Here the fat is fried.
And nothing's overlooked
Till I'm satisfied.

Food beyond compare,
Food beyond belief,
Mix it in a mincer and pretend it's beef.
Kidney of a horse,
Liver of a cat,
Filling up the sausages with this and that.
Residents are more than welcome.
Bridal suite is occupied.
Reasonable charges,
Plus some little extras on the side.

Charge 'em for the lice,
Extra for the mice,
Two percent for looking in the mirror twice.
Here a little slice,
There a little cut,
Three per cent for sleeping with the window shut.
When it comes to fixing prices,
There are lots of tricks he knows.
How it all increases,
All them bits and pieces,
But here we strive to lighten your purse.
Jesus, it's amazing how it grows!

Refrain

Madame Thernardier:
I used to dream that I would meet a prince.
But, God Almighty,
Have you seen what's happened since?
Master of the house?
Isn't worth my spit!
Comforter, philosopher and lifelong shit!

Cunning little brain,

Regular Voltaire.
Thinks he's quite a lover but there's not much
  there!
What a cruel trick of nature
Landed me with such a louse.
God knows how I've lasted
Living with this bastard in the house!

Refrain:
Master of the house,
Master and a half,
Comforter, philosopher—don't make me laugh!
Servant to the poor,
Butler to the great,
Hypocrite and toady and inebriate!
Ev'rybody bless our landlord.
Ev'rybody bless his spouse.
Thernardier:
Ev'rybody raise a glass,

Madame Thernardier:
Raise it up the master's ass!

All:
Ev'rybody raise a glass
To the master of the house!

Maybe This Time

Words by Fred Ebb
Music by John Kander

from *Cabaret*

Maybe this time,
I'll be lucky.
Maybe this time he'll stay.
Maybe this time,
For the first time,
Love won't hurry away.
He will hold me fast.
I'll be home at last.
Not a loser anymore,
Like the last time and the time before.

Everybody
Loves a winner
So nobody loved me.
Lady Peaceful.
Lady Happy
That's what I long to be.
All the odds are
In my favor
Something's bound to begin.
It's got to happen,
Happen sometime;
Maybe this time I'll win.

Repeat Verse 2

Me & My Girl

Words by Douglas Furber & Arthur Rose
Music by Noel Gay

from *Me & My Girl*

Life's an empty thing,
Life can be so awful lonesome,
If you're always on your own some,
Life's an empty thing.

Life's a diff'rent thing,
When you've found your one and only,
Then you feel no longer lonely,
Life's a happy thing.

Ev'rything was topsy-turvy,
Life seemed all wrong,
But it came all right
As soon as you came along.

Me and my girl,
Meant for each other,
Sent for each other,
And liking it so.
Me and my girl,
'Sno use pretending,
We knew the ending
A long time ago.

Some little clown,
With a big steeple,
Just a few people
That both of us know.
And we'll have love,
Laughter,
Be happy ever after,
Me and my girl.

Mein Herr

Words by Fred Ebb
Music by John Kander

from *Cabaret*

You have to understand the way I am,
   mein Herr.
A tiger is a tiger, not a lamb, mein Herr.
You'll never turn the vinegar to jam,
   mein Herr.
So I do what I do.
When I'm through, then I'm through,
And I'm through. Toodle-oo!

Refrain 1:
Bye bye, mein lieber Herr,
Farewell mein lieber Herr,
It was a fine affair,
But now it's over.
And though I used to care,
I need the open air,
You're better off without me,
Mein Herr.

Refrain 2:
Don't dab your eye, mein Herr,
Or wonder why, mein Herr,
I've always said that I
Was a rover.
You musn't knit your brow.
You should have known by now
You'd ev'ry cause to doubt me,
Mein Herr.

The continent of Europe is so wide,
   mein Herr.
Not only up and down, but side to side,
   mein Herr.
I couldn't ever cross it if I tried, mein Herr.
But I do what I can,
Inch by inch, step by step,
Mile by mile, man by man.

Refrain 1

Refrain 2

Bye bye mein lieber Herr,
Auf wiedersehen, mein Herr.
Es war sehr gut, mein Herr,
Und vorbei.
Du kennst mich wohl, mein Herr,
Ach, lebe wohl, mein Herr.
Du sollst mich nie mehr sehen,
Mein Herr.

Refrain 1

You'll get on without me,
Mein Herr.

Memory

Music by Andrew Lloyd Webber
Text by Trevor Nunn after T.S. Eliot

from *Cats*

Midnight.
Not a sound from the pavement.
Has the moon lost her memory?
She is smiling alone.
In the lamp-light
The withered leaves collect at my feet
And the wind
Begins to moan.

Memory.
All alone in the moonlight
I can smile at the old days,
I was beautiful then.
I remember
The time I knew what happiness was,
Let the memory
Live again.

Ev'ry street lamp seems to beat
A fatalistic warning.
Someone mutters
And a street lamp gutters
And soon it will be morning.

Daylight.
I must wait for the sunrise.
I must think of a new life
And I mustn't give in.
When the dawn comes
Tonight will be a memory too
And a new day
Will begin.

Burnt out ends of smoky days
The stale cold smell of the morning;
The street lamp dies
Another night is over,
Another day is dawning.

Touch me.
It's so easy to leave me
All alone with the memory
Of my days in the sun.
If you touch me
You'll understand what happiness is.
Look, a new day
Has begun.

Mister Snow

Lyrics by Oscar Hammerstein II
Music by Richard Rodgers

from *Carousel*

His name is Mister Snow,
And an upstandin' man is he.
He comes home ev'ry night in his
   round-bottomed boat,
With a net full of herring from the sea.

An almost perfect beau,
As refined as a girl could wish,
But he spends so much time in his
   round-bottomed boat,
That he can't seem to lose the smell of fish!

The fust time he kissed me,
   the whiff of his clo'es
Knocked me flat on the floor of the room,
But now that I love him,
   my heart's in my nose,
And fish is my fav'rite perfume!

Last night he spoke quite low,
And a fair spoken man is he,
And he said, "Miss Pipperidge, I'd like it fine
If I could be wed with a wife,
And, indeed, Miss Pipperidge,
   if you'll be mine,
I'll be yours fer the rest of my life!"

Next moment we were promised!
And now my mind's in a maze,
Fer all it ken do is look forward to
That wonderful day of days.

When I marry Mister Snow,
The flowers'll be buzzin' with the
   hum of bees,
The birds'll make a racket in the
   churchyard trees,
When I marry Mister Snow.

Then it's off to home we'll go,
And both of us'll look a little dreamy-eyed,
A-drivin' to a cottage by the ocean side,
Where the salty breezes blow.

He'll carry me 'cross the threshold,
And I'll be as meek as a lamb.
Then he'll set me on my feet,
And I'll say, kinda sweet,
Spoken:
"Well, Mister Snow, here I am!"

Then I'll kiss him so he'll know
That ev'rythin' 'll be as right as right ken be,
A-livin' in a cottage by the sea with me,
For I love that Mister Snow,
That young, seafarin', bold and darin',
Big, bewhiskered, over bearin' darlin',
Mister Snow!

More Than You Know

Words by William Rose & Edward Eliscu
Music by Vincent Youmans

from *Great Day!*

Whether you are here or yonder,
Whether you are false or true,
Whether you remain or wander
I'm growing fonder of you.

Even though your friends forsake you,
Even though you don't succeed,
Wouldn't I be glad to take you,
Give you the break you need.

More than you know,
More than you know,
Man o' my heart, I love you so.
Lately I find you're on my mind,
More than you know.

Whether you're right,
Whether you're wrong,
Man o' my heart I'll string along.
You need me so
More than you'll ever know.

Loving you the way that I do
There's nothing I can do about it,
Loving may be all you can give
But honey, I can't live without it.

Oh, how I'd cry,
Oh, how I'd cry,
If you got tired and said, "Goodbye,"
More than I'd show
More than you'd ever know.

Money, Money, Money

Words & Music by Benny Andersson & Björn Ulvaeus

from *Mamma Mia!*

Donna:
I work all night, I work all day,
To pay the bills I have to pay,

Company:
Ain't it sad?

Donna:
But still there never seems to be
A single penny left for me.

Company:
That's too bad.

Donna:
In my dreams I have a plan;
If I got me a wealthy man,
I wouldn't have to work at all,
I'd fool around and have a ball.

Company:
Money, money, money,
Must be funny,
In a rich man's world.
Money, money, money,
Always sunny,
In a rich man's world.

Ah ha, all the things I could do
If I had a little money,
It's a rich man's world.
It's a rich man's world.

Tanya:
A man like that is hard to find

Donna:
But I can't get him off my mind,

Company:
Ain't it sad?

Rosie:
And if he happened to be free
I bet he wouldn't fancy me.

Company:
That's too bad.

Pepper:
So I must leave, I have to go
To Las Vegas or Monaco
And win a fortune in a game,
My life would never be the same…

Company:
Money, money, money,
Must be funny,
In a rich man's world.
Money, money, money,
Always sunny,
In a rich man's world.

Donna:
Ah ha, all the things I could do

Company:
If I had a little money,
It's a rich man's world.

Money, money, money,
Must be funny,
In a rich man's world.
Money, money, money,
Always sunny,
In a rich man's world.

Donna:
Ah ha, all the things I could do

Company:
If I had a little money,
It's a rich man's world.
It's a rich man's world.

Money, Money

Music by John Kander
Lyrics by Fred Ebb

from *Cabaret*

Money makes the world go around,
The world go around, the world go around,
Money makes the world go around,
It makes the world go round.

Boy:
  Girl:
A mark, a yen, a buck or a pound,
A buck or a pound, a buck or a pound
A mark, a yen, a buck or a pound

Boy:
Is all that makes the world go around,
That clinking, clanking sound can make the
   world go round.

Both:
Money, money, money, money,
Money, money, money, money,
Money, money, money, money,

Boy:
  Girl:
If you happen to be rich,
  Money, money, money, money,
And you feel like tonight's entertainment,
  Money, money, money, money,
You can pay for a gay escapade.
  Money, money, money, money,

  Money, money, money, money,
If you happen to be rich, and alone,
  Money, money, money, money,
And you need a companion,
  Money, money, money, money,
You can ring ting- a- ling for the maid.
  Money, money, money, money,

  Money, money, money, money,
If you happen to be rich
And you find you are left by your lover,
  Money, money, money, money,
Tho you moan and groan quite a lot
  Money, money, money, money,
You can take it on the chin,
  Money, money, money, money,
Call a cab, and begin to recover
  Mon.
On your fourteen carat yacht.

    What?

Both:
Money makes the world go around,
The world go around, the world go around.
Money makes the world go around.
Of that we both are sure.
(Raspberry) On being poor.

Money, money, money, money,
Money, money, money, money,
Money, money, money, money,
Mon.

When you haven't any coal in the stove
And you freeze in the winter
And you curse to the wind at your fate.
When you haven't any shoes on your feet
And your coat's thin as paper
And you look thirty pounds under-weight.
When you go to get a word of advice from the
    fat little pastor,
He will tell you to love evermore.
But when hunger comes to rap,
Rat-a-tat rat-a-tat, at the window,
See how love flies out the door.

For money makes the world go around,
The world go around, the world go around.
Money makes the world go around,
The clinking, clanking sound of
Money, money, money, money,
Money, money, money, money,

Get a little, get a little,
Money, money, money, money,
Mark, a yen, a buck or a pound
That clinking, clanking clunking sound
Is all that makes the world go round,
It makes the world go round.

Mountain Duet

Words & Music by Benny Andersson, Tim Rice & Björn Ulvaeus

from *Chess*

Florence:
This is the one situation
I wanted most to avoid.
Nothing I say will convince him it isn't a trick.

The Russian:
A drink on a clear moonlight night.
I relax, she smiles.
There's something unpleasant going on.

Florence:
So with immaculate timing
I'm left to carry the can.
Embarrassed, outnumbered, marooned.

The Russian:
Now she can't be working for them,
I mean us,
She seems so very straight forward,
But where is he?

Florence:
He has to come back
He wanted this meeting, well, didn't he?

The Russian:
Maybe he's scared,
Just as scared as he was in the game.

Florence:
Oh, I just couldn't care less.
He can go right ahead,
Go and wreck his career,
I know I've done my best.

The Russian:
Well, at least she's a good-looking spy.

Florence:
What if my Russian friend thinks that my plans
Are more of an intimate kind.
If I don't say something else soon he'll go-
Nobody's on nobody's side!

The Russian:
Listen, I hate to break up the mood.
Get to the point, begin the beguine.
Haven't you noticed we're a protagonist short
In this idyllic, well produced scene?

Florence:
All I can say is moments ago
He was right here ready and waiting.

The Russian:
Never mind him, I haven't missed him so far.
Maybe it won't do any harm
To struggle on without his charm.
Funny how all at once I feel that
He can go jump off the mountain; I won't care.

Florence:
This is the one situation
I wanted most to avoid.

The Russian:
My dear opponent, I really can't imagine why.

Florence:
So I am not dangerous then? What a shame!

The Russian:
Oh, you're not dangerous,
Who could think that of you?

Florence:
You, you are so strange
Why can't you be what you ought to be?

Both:
You should be scheming,
Intriguing, too clever by half.

The Russian:
I have to hand it to you,
For you managed to make me forget
Why I ever agreed to this farce.

Both:
I don't know why I can't think of anything I
    would rather do
Than be wasting my time on mountains with
    you.

Mr. Wonderful

Words & Music by Jerry Bock, Larry Holofcener & George David Weiss

from *Mr. Wonderful*

Why this feeling?
Why this glow?
Why the thrill when you say, "Hello!"?
It's a strange and tender magic you do.
Mr. Wonderful,
That's you!

Why this trembling when you speak?
Why this joy when you touch my cheek?
I must tell you what my heart knows is true:
Mr. Wonderful, that's you!

And why this longing to know your charms;
To spend forever here in your arms!
Oh! there's much more I could say,
But the words keep slipping away;
And I'm left with only one point of view:
Mr. Wonderful,
That's you!

One more thing, then I'm through;
Mr. Wonderful,
Mr. Wonderful,
Mr. Wonderful, I love you!

The Music Of The Night

Music by Andrew Lloyd Webber
Lyrics by Charles Hart
Additional Lyrics by Richard Stilgoe

from *The Phantom Of The Opera*

Night-time sharpens, heightens each sensation;
Darkness stirs and wakes imagination.
Silently the senses abandon their defenses.

Slowly, gently night unfurls its splendor;
Grasp it, sense it, tremulous and tender.
Turn your face away from the garish light of
  day,
Turn your thoughts away from cold unfeeling
  light
And listen to the music of the night.

Close your eyes and surrender to your darkest
  dreams!
Purge your thoughts of the life you knew
  before!
Close your eyes, let your spirit start to soar,
And you'll live as you've never lived before.

Softly, deftly, music shall caress you.
Hear it, feel it secretly possess you.
Open up your mind, let your fantasies unwind
In this darkness which you know you cannot
  fight,
The darkness of the music of the night.

Let your mind start a journey through a strange,
  new world;
Leave all thoughts of the world you knew
  before.
Let your soul take you where you long to be!
Only then can you belong to me.

Floating, falling, sweet intoxication.
Touch me, trust me, savour each sensation.
Let the dream begin, let your darker side give
  in
To the power of the music that I write,
The power of the music of the night.

You alone can make my song take flight,
Help me make the music of the night.

My Favorite Things

Lyrics by Oscar Hammerstein II
Music by Richard Rodgers

from *The Sound Of Music*

Raindrops on roses and whiskers on kittens.
Bright copper kettles and warm woollen
    mittens.
Brown paper packages tied up with strings,
These are a few of my favorite things.

Cream-colored ponies and crisp apple strudels,
Doorbells and sleigh-bells and schnitzel with
    noodles,
Wild geese that fly with the moon on their
    wings,
These are a few of my favorite things.

Girls in white dresses with blue satin sashes,
Snowflakes that stay on my nose and eyelashes,
Silver white winters that melt into springs,
These are a few of my favorites things.

When the dog bites,
When the bees stings,
When I'm feeling sad,
I simply remember my favorite things
And then I don't feel so bad!

My Funny Valentine

Words by Lorenz Hart
Music by Richard Rodgers

from *Babes In Arms*

Behold the way our fine-feathered friend
His virtue doth parade.
Though knowest not, my dim-witted friend,
The picture thou hast made.
Thy vacant brow and thy tousled hair
Conceal thy good intent.
Thou noble, upright, truthful, sincere,
And slightly dopey gent, you're...

My funny Valentine,
Sweet comic Valentine,
You make me smile with my heart.
Your looks are laughable,
Unphotographable,
Yet you're my favorite work of art.
Is your figure less than Greek?
Is your mouth a little weak?
When you open it to speak
Are you smart?
But don't change a hair for me,
Not if you care for me,
Stay, little Valentine, stay!
Each day is Valentine's Day.

My Husband Makes Movies

Words & Music by Maury Yeston

from *Nine*

My husband makes movies.
To make them, he lives a kind of dream,
In which his actions aren't always
    what they seem.
He may be on to some unique
    romantic theme.

Some men catch fish,
Some men tie flies,
Some earn their living baking bread.
My husband, he goes a little crazy,
Making movies instead.

My husband spins fantasies.
He lives them, then gives them to you all.
While he was working on the film on
    ancient Rome,
He made the slave girls take the
    gladiators home.

Some men buy stocks,
Some men punch clocks,
Some leap where others fear to tread.
My husband, as author and director,
Makes up stories in his head.

Guido Contini, Luisa Contini,
Number one genius and number one fan.
Guido Contini, Luisa Contini,
Daughter of well-to-do Florentine clan,
Long ago, twenty years ago.

Once the names were,
Guido Contini, Luisa Del Forno,
Actress with dreams and a life of her own.
Passionate, wild, and in love with Livorno,
Singing with Guido all night on the phone,
Long ago, someone else ago.
How he needs me so,
And he'll be the last to know it.

My husband makes movies,
To make them, he makes himself obsessed.
He works for weeks on end,
    without a bit of rest,
No other way can he achieve his level best.

Some men read books,
Some shine their shoes,
Some retire early,
When they've seen the evening news.
My husband only rarely comes to bed,
My husband makes movies instead.
My husband makes movies.

My Time Of Day

Words & Music by Frank Loesser

from *Guys & Dolls*

My time of day is the dark-time,
A couple of deals before dawn,
When the street belongs to the cop,
And the janitor with the mop,
And the grocery clerks are all gone.
When the smell of the rain-washed pavement
Comes up clean and fresh and cold,
And the street lamplight
Fills the gutter with gold,
That's my time of day,
My time of day,
And you're the only doll I've ever wanted,
To share it with me.

The Name Of The Game

Words & Music by Benny Andersson, Björn Ulvaues & Stig Anderson

from *Mamma Mia!*

Sophie:
I've seen you twice, in a short time
Only a day since we started
It seems to me, for every time
I'm getting more open-hearted.

Your smile and the sound of your voice,
And the way you see through me.
Got a feeling, you give me no choice,
But it means a lot to me,

So I wanna know
What's the name of the game?
Does it mean anything to you?

What's the name of the game?
Can you feel it the way I do?

Tell me please, 'cause I have to know,
I'm a curious child, beginning to grow.

And you make me talk
And you make me feel
And you make me sure
What I'm trying to conceal.

If I trust in you
Would you let me down?
Would you laugh at me
If I said I care for you?
Could you feel the same way too?

I wanna know
What's the name of the game?

Bill:
 I'll talk to your mother tonight.

Sophie:
Does it mean anything to you?

Bill:
Gotta trust me, I 'm doing what's right.
And it means a lot.

Sophie:
What's the name of the game?

Bill:
Your smile and the sound of your voice.

Sophie:
Can you feel it the way I do?

Tell me please, 'cause I have to know,
I'm a curious child, beginning to grow.
And you make me talk
And you make me feel
And you make me show
What I'm trying to conceal.

If I trust in you
Would you let me down?
Would you laugh at me
If I said I cared for you?
Would you feel the same way too?

I wanna know
What's the name of the game?

Bill:
I'll talk to your mother today.

Sophie:
Does it mean anything to you?

Bill:
 Just give me an hour, ok?.
And it means a lot.

Sophie:
What's the name of the game?
Do you feel the way I do?

I wanna know,
Oh yes, I wanna know
What's the name of the game?

Never Will I Marry

Words & Music by Frank Loesser

from *Greenwillow*

Any flimsy dimsy looking for true love
Better smile me no good, dearie, good day.
Any flimsy dimsy looking for true love
Better look her looking some other way,
For my kiss can be no evermore promise,
But a fancy dancy fiddle and free.
Any flimsy dimsy looking for true love
Better waste no time, no time on me.

Never, never will I marry,
Never, never will I wed.
Born to wander solitary,
Wide my world, narrow my bed.
Never, never, never will I marry,
Born to wander 'til I'm dead.

No burdens to bear,
No conscience nor care,
No mem'ries to mourn,
No turning, for I was:

Born to wander solitary,
Wide my world, narrow my bed.
Never, never, never will I marry,
Born to wander 'til I'm dead.

A New Life

Words by Leslie Bricusse
Music by Frank Wildhorn

from *Jekyll & Hyde*

A new life,
What I wouldn't give to have a new life!
One thing I learned as I go through life,
Nothing is for free along the way!

A new start,
That's the thing I need to give me new heart.
Half a chance in life to find a new part,
Just a simple role that I can play.

A new hope,
Something to convince me to renew hope!
A new day,
Bright enough to help me find my way!
A new chance,
One that maybe has a touch of romance.
Where can it be?
The chance for me?

A new dream,
I have one I know that very few dream!
I would like to see that overdue dream,
Even though it never may come true!

A new love,
Though I know there's no such thing as true
  love.
Even so, although I never knew love,
Still I feel that one dream is my due!
A new world,
This one thing I want to ask of you, world.
Once! Before it's time to bid adieu, world!
One sweet chance to prove the cynics wrong!

A new life,
More and more I'm sure, as I go through life,
Just to play the game and to pursue life,
Just to share its pleasures and belong!
That's what I've been here for all along!
Each day's a brand new life!

No Other Love

Lyrics by Oscar Hammerstein II
Music by Richard Rodgers

from *Me & Juliet*

No other love have I,
Only my love for you,
Only the dream we knew,
No other love.

Watching the night go by,
Wishing that you could be
Watching the night with me,
Into the night I cry:
Hurry home, come home to me!
Set me free,
Free from doubt,
And free from longing.

Into your arms I'll fly.
Locked in your arms I'll stay,
Waiting to hear you say:
No other love have I,
No other love.

Nobody's Heart

Words by Lorenz Hart
Music by Richard Rodgers

from *By Jupiter*

Refrain:
Nobody's heart belongs to me,
Heigh-ho!
Who cares?
Nobody writes his songs to me,
No one belongs to me,
That's the least of my cares.

I may be sad at times,
And disinclined to play,
But, it's not bad at times,
To go your own sweet way.

Nobody's arms belong to me,
No arms feel strong to me,
I admire the moon,
As a moon,
Just a moon,
Nobody's heart belongs to me today.

Refrain

Ride, Amazon ride.
Hunt your stags and bears.
Take life in its stride.
Heigh-ho!
Who cares?
Go hunting with pride,
Track bears to their lairs.
Ride, Amazon ride!
Heigh-ho,
Who cares?

Refrain

Nothing

Words by Edward Kleban
Music by Marvin Hamlisch

from *A Chorus Line*

Spoken:
I mean, I was dying to be a serious actress.
Anyway, it's the first day of acting class,
And we're in the auditorium
And the teacher, Mister Karp,
Puts us up on the stage
With our legs around everybody,
One in back of the other,
And he says: O.K., we're gonna do
    improvisations.
Now, you're on a bobsled and it's
    snowing out.
And it's cold. O.K., go!

Sung:
Ev'ry day for a week
We would try to feel the motion,
Feel the motion,
Down the hill.
Ev'ry day for a week
We would try to hear the wind rush,
Hear the wind rush,
Feel the chill.

And I dug right down to the bottom
    of my soul,
To see what I had inside.
Yes, I dug right down to the bottom
    of my soul,
And I tried; I tried.

Spoken:
Everyone is going:
Whoosh! I feel the snow,
I feel the cold—the air.
And Mr. Karp turns to me and says:
O.K., Morales, what did you feel?

Sung:
And I said, "Nothing,
I'm feeling nothing,"
And he says, "Nothing
Could get a girl transferred!"
They all felt something,
But I felt nothing,
Except the feeling
That this bullshit was absurd!

Spoken:
But I said to myself:
"Hey, it's only the first week.
Maybe it's genetic.
They don't have bobsleds in San Juan."

Sung:
Second week, more advanced,
And we had to be a table,
Be a sports car,
Ice cream cone.
Mister Karp, he would say,
"Very good, except Morales.
Try, Morales.
All alone."

'Cause I felt—nothing.

So I dug right down to the bottom
   of my soul,
To see how an ice cream felt.
Yes, I dug right down to the bottom
   of my soul,
And I tried to melt.

The kids yelled, "Nothing!"
They called me "Nothing!"
And Karp allowed it,
Which really makes me burn.

They were so helpful,
They called me hopeless,
Until I really didn't know
Where else to turn!

Spoken:
And Karp kept saying,
"Morales, I think you should
Transfer to girls' high.
You'll never be an actress. Never!"

Jesus Christ!

Sung:
Went to church praying,
"Santa Maria, send me guidance,
Send me guidance."
On my knees.
Went to church praying,
"Santa Maria, help me feel it,
Help me feel it.
Pretty please!"

And a voice from down at the bottom
   of my soul,
Came up to the top of my head.
And the voice from down at the bottom
   of my soul,
Here is what it said:

"This man is nothing!
This course is nothing!
If you want something,
Go find a better class.
And when you find one,
You'll be an actress."
And I assure you that's what
Fin'lly came to pass.

Six months later I heard that Karp had died.
And I dug right down to the bottom
   of my soul,
And cried,
'Cause I felt—nothing.

Now That I've Seen Her

Music by Claude-Michel Schönberg
Lyrics by Richard Maltby Jr. & Alain Boublil

from *Miss Saigon*

There are days.
There are days when your life clouds over,
And the world gets so dark
That all at once you can't tell night from day.
There are times when your heart cries it isn't
   happening.
But the truth is cold and real,
And I know this storm won't go away.

Now that I've seen her there's no way to hide,
She is not some fling from long ago.
Now that I've seen her I know why he lied,
And I think it was better when I didn't know.

In her eyes, in her voice,
In the heat that filled the air
Part of him still lingers there.
I know what pain her life today must be.
But if it all comes down to her or me,
I won't wait, I swear I'll fight.

Now that I've seen her she's more than a name
She is not some fling from long ago.
Now that I've seen her I can't stay the same.
Who's the man that I always trusted.
Now I have to know.

Oh, What A Beautiful Mornin'

Lyrics by Oscar Hammerstein II
Music by Richard Rodgers

from *Oklahoma!*

There's a bright golden haze on the meadow,
There's a bright golden haze on the meadow.
The corn is as high as an elephant's eye,
An' it looks like it's climbin' clear up to the sky.

Refrain:
Oh, what a beautiful mornin'!
Oh, what a beautiful day!
I got a beautiful feelin'
Everything's goin' my way.

All the cattle are standin' like statues,
All the cattle are standin' like statues.
They don't turn their heads as they see me ride
   by,
But a little brown maverick is winkin' her eye.

Refrain

All the sounds of the earth are like music,
All the sounds of the earth are like music.
The breeze is so busy it don't miss a tree,
And a ol' weepin' willer is laughin' at me.

Refrain

Oh, what a beautiful day!

Oklahoma

Lyrics by Oscar Hammerstein II
Music by Richard Rodgers

from *Oklahoma!*

They couldn't pick a better time to start in life,
It ain't too early and it ain't too late.
Startin' as a farmer with a brand-new wife,
Soon be livin' in a brand-new state!
Brand-new state
Gonna treat you great!

Gonna give you barley,
Carrots and pertaters,
Pasture fer the cattle,
Spinach and termayters!
Flowers on the prairie where the June bugs
    zoom,
Plen'y of air and plen'y of room,
Plen'y of room to swing a rope,
Plen'y of heart and plen'y of hope.

Oklahoma,
Where the wind comes sweepin' down the plain
(And the wavin' wheat
Can sure smell sweet
When the wind comes right behind the rain)
Oklahoma!
Every night my honey lamb and I
Sit alone and talk
And watch a hawk
Makin' lazy circles in the sky.
We know we belong to the land,
And the land we belong to is grand.
And when we say:
Ee-ee-ow! A-yip-i-o-ee-ay!
We're only sayin',
You're doin' fine, Oklahoma!
Oklahoma, O.K.!

An Old Man

Lyrics by Martin Charnin
Music by Richard Rodgers

from *Two By Two*

An old man is queer in his ways,
His appetite fails,
But he's hungry for praise.
And the sights that he's seen
Cloud the sights that he'll see.
Old isn't easy to be.

An old man gets cranky at night,
When barrels won't lift
And an apple won't bite.
When what used to be sure
Has a whole other face,
Old is an unfriendly place.

He walks like he's smoothing out bumps in a
    rug,
For hours he'll stare at a spot.
The hug that he gives you is hardly a hug,
You remember the hug that it's not anymore.

An old man, he's sometimes afraid;
He sings to the sun,
But he's partial to shade.
To himself, he's a wit,
To the world he's a pest!
Old isn't what he does best.

An old man, he shivers in bed,
It's all of the years
That have spun 'round his head.
He's the burdensome thing
That a fam'ly ignores.
He's to put in a room
And to lock all the doors—
Except—
Except—
Except when an old man is yours.

Ol' Man River

Music by Jerome Kern
Lyrics by Oscar Hammerstein II

from *Showboat*

Coloured folks on de Mississippi,
Coloured folks work while de white folks play.
Pullin' dose boats from de dawn to sunset,
Gittin' no rest till de judgment day.

Don't look up an' don't look down,
You don't dast make de white boss frown;
Bend yo' knees an' bow yo' head,
An' pull dat rope until you're dead.

Let me go 'way from de Mississippi,
Let me go 'way from de white men boss.
Show me dat stream called de river Jordan,
Dat's de ol' stream dat I long to cross.

Ol' man river, dat ol' man river,
He must know sumpin',
But don't say nothin',
He jus' keeps rollin',
He keeps on rollin' along.
He don't plant 'taters, he don't plant cotton,
An' dem dat plants 'em is soon forgotten;
But ol' man river, he jus' keeps rollin along.

You an' me, we sweat and strain,
Body all achin' an' racked wid pain.
"Tote dat barge!" "Lift dat bale,"
Git a little drunk an' you land in jail.
Ah gits weary an' sick of tryin',
Ah'm tired of livin' an' skeered of dyin'
But ol' man river he jus' keeps rollin along.

On My Own

Music by Claude-Michel Schönberg
Original Lyrics by Alain Boublil & Jean-Marc Natel
English Lyrics by Herbert Kretzmer, Trevor Nunn & John Caird

from *Les Misérables*

On my own, pretending he's beside me.
All alone, I walk with him 'til morning.
Without him, I feel his arms around me.
And when I lose my way,
I close my eyes and he has found me.

In the rain, the pavement shines like silver.
All the lights are misty in the river.
In the darkness the trees are full of starlight.
And all I see is him and me forever and forever.

And I know it's only in my mind
That I'm talking to myself and not to him.
And although I know that he is blind,
Still I say there's a way for us.

I love him, but when the night is over,
He is gone, the river's just a river.
Without him the world around me changes.
The trees are bare
And everywhere the streets are full of strangers.

I love him but every day I'm learning,
All my life I've only been pretending.
Without me his world will go on turning.
The world is full of happiness that I have never
    known.

I love him,
I love him,
I love him,
But only on my own.

On The Street Where You Live

Words by Alan Jay Lerner
Music by Frederick Loewe

from *My Fair Lady*

I have often walked
Down this street before
But the pavement always stayed beneath my feet
   before.
All at once am I,
Several stories high,
Knowing I'm on the street where you live.

Are there lilac trees
In the heart of town?
Can you hear a lark in any other part of town?
Does enchantment pour
Out of every door?
No, it's just on the street where you live.

And oh, the towering feeling,
Just to know somehow you are near!
The overpowering feeling
That any second you may suddenly appear!

People stop and stare,
They don't bother me;
For there's nowhere else on earth that I would
   rather be.

Let the time go by,
I won't care if I
Can be here on the street where you live.

On The Willows

Words &Music by Stephen Schwartz

from *Godspell*

Refrain:
On the willows there,
We hung up our lyres.
For our captors there
Required of us songs,
And our tormentors, mirth.

Refrain

Saying,
"Sing us one of the songs of Zion,
Sing us one of the songs of Zion,
Sing us one of the songs of Zion,"
But how can we sing,
Sing the Lord's song,
In a foreign land?

On the willows there,
We hung up our lyres.

Once In Love With Amy

Words & Music by Frank Loesser

from *Where's Charley?*

I caught you, sir,
Having a look at her,
As she went strolling by.
Now, didn't your heart go boom,
Boom, boom, boom, boom?
Now didn't you hear a sigh?

I warn you, sir,
Don't start to dream of her,
Just bid such thoughts be gone,
Or it will be boom, boom,
Boom, boom, boom, boom,
Boom, boom, boom, boom, boom,
From then on.

For, once in love with Amy,
Always in love with Amy,
Ever and ever fascinated by her,
Sets your heart afire to stay.

Once you're kiss'd by Amy,
Tear up your list, it's Amy,
Ply her with bonbons, poetry and flowers,
Moon a million hours away.

You might be quite the fickle hearted rover,
So carefree, and bold,
Who loves a girl, and later thinks it over,
And just quits cold.

Ah, but once in love with Amy,
Always in love with Amy,
Ever and ever,
Sweetly you'll romance her,
Trouble is, the answer will be,
(Laughs) Ha, ha, ha, ha,
That Amy'd rather stay in love with me!

Once Upon A Dream

Words by Steve Cuden, Leslie Bricusse & Frank Wildhorn
Music by Frank Wildhorn

from *Jekyll & Hyde*

When this all began,
I knew there'd be a price.

Once upon a dream,
I was lost in love's embrace.
There I found a perfect place,
Once upon a dream.

Once there was a time
Like no other time before,
Hope was still an open door,
Once upon a dream.

And I was unafraid,
The dream was so exciting!
But now I see it fade,
And I am here alone!

Once upon a dream,
You were heaven sent to me,
Was it never meant to be?
Are you just a dream?
Could we begin again,
Once upon a dream?

Once You Lose Your Heart

Words & Music by Noel Gay

from *Me & My Girl*

Once you lose your heart,
Once somebody takes it,
From the place it rested in before.
Once you lose your heart,
Once somebody wakes it,
Then it isn't your heart any more.

Refrain:
It's gone before you knew
It could ever go that way,
And now you must pursue it,
Forever and a day.

Once you lose your heart,
Once somebody takes it,
There's one thing certain from the start,
You'll find forever,
You've got to follow your heart.

They say a girl should never be without love,
And all the joy that love alone can bring.
All that I have ever learnt about love,
Tells me it's a very funny thing.
For when your heart is fancy-free,
You hope some man will choose it,
But oh, the spin you'll find you're in,
The very moment that you lose it.

Once you lose your heart,
Once somebody takes it,
From the place it rested in before.
Once you lose your heart,
Once somebody takes it,
Then it isn't your heart any more.

Refrain

Once you lose your heart,
Once somebody takes it,
There's one thing certain from the start,
You've got to follow,
You've got to follow your heart.

One

Music by Marvin Hamlisch
Lyric by Edward Kleban

from *A Chorus Line*

One
Singular sensation
Every step that she takes.
One
Thrilling combination
Every move that she makes.
One smile and suddenly nobody else will do.
You know you'll never be lonely with you-know-
    who.

One
Moment in her presence
And you can forget the rest.
For the girl is second best to none, son.
Ooh! Sigh!
Give her your attention,
Do I really have to mention
She's the one?

One Night In Bangkok

Words & Music by Benny Andersson, Tim Rice & Björn Ulvaeus

from *Chess*

The American:
Bangkok! Oriental setting
And the city don't know what the city is getting,
The crème de la crème of the chess world
In a show with everything but Yul Brynner.
And thank God I'm only watching the game,
Controlling it.

Time flies doesn't seem a minute
Since the Tirolean spa had the chess boys in it.
All change - don't you know that when you play
   at this level
There's no ordinary venue.
It's Iceland or the Philippines or Hastings or -
   or this place!

Choir:
One night in Bangkok and the world's your
   oyster,
The bars are temples but the pearls ain't free.
You'll find a god in every golden cloister
And if you're lucky then the god's a she.
I can feel an angel sliding up to me.

The American:
One town's very like another
When your head's down over your pieces,
   brother.

Choir:
It's a drag, it's a bore, it's really such a pity
To be looking at the board, not looking at the
   city.

The American:
Whaddy-a mean?
You've seen one crowded, polluted, stinking
   town,
You've see them all!

Choir:
Tea, girls warm and sweet
Some are set up in the Somerset Maugham
   suite.

The American:
Get Thai'd! You're talking to a tourist
Whose every move's among the purest.
I get my kicks above the waistline, sunshine!

Choir:
One night in Bangkok makes a hard man
   humble,
Not much between despair and ecstasy.
One night in Bangkok and the tough guys
   tumble.
Can't be too careful with your company.
I can feel the devil walking next to me.

The American:

Siam's gonna be the witness
To the ultimate test of cerebral fitness.
This grips me more than would a muddy old
    river or reclining Buddah.
And thank God I'm only watching the game,
    controlling it.
I don't see you guys rating the kind of mate I'm
    contemplating.
I'd let you watch, I would invite you
But the queens we use would not excite you.
So you'd better go back to your bars, your
    temples, your massage parlours.

Choir:

One night in Bangkok and the world's your
    oyster,
The bars are temples but the pearls ain't free.
You'll find a god in every golden cloister,
A little flesh, a little history.
I can feel an angel sliding up to me.

One night in Bangkok makes a hard man
    humble,
Not much between despair and ecstasy.
One night in Bangkok and the tough guys
    tumble,
Can't be too careful with your company.
I can feel the devil walking next to me.

Our Language Of Love

Music by Marguerite Monnot
Original French Words by Alexandre Breffort
English Words by Julian More, David Heneker & Monty Norman

from *Irma La Douce*

No need to speak,
No need to sing,
When just a glance means ev'rything.
Not a word need be spoken,
In our language of love.

I'll touch your cheek,
You'll hold my hand,
And only we will understand
That the silence is broken,
By our language of love.

It's clear to you,
It's clear to me,
This precious moment had to be,
Other moments outclassing,
Guardian angels are passing.

No words will do,
No lips can say
The tender meaning we convey,
"I love you" is unspoken,
In our language of love.

Out Of My Dreams

Lyrics by Oscar Hammerstein II
Music by Richard Rodgers

from *Oklahoma!*

Refrain:
Out of my dreams and into your arms I long to
    fly.
I will come as evening comes to woo a waiting
    sky.
Out of my dreams and into the hush of falling
    shadows,
When the mist is low and stars are breaking
    through,
Then out of my dreams I'll go
Into a dream with you.

Won't have to make up any more stories, you'll
    be there!
Think of the bright midsummer night glories we
    can share.
Won't have to go on kissing a daydream, I'll
    have you.
You'll be real, real as the white moon lighting
    the blue.

Refrain

People Will Say We're In Love

Lyrics by Oscar Hammerstein II
Music by Richard Rodgers

from *Oklahoma!*

Verse (Girl):
Why do they think up stories that link my name
    with yours?
Why do the neighbors chatter all day,
    behind their doors?
I know a way to prove what they say is
    quite untrue.
Here is the gist, a practical list of "don'ts" for
    you.

Refrain:
Don't throw bouquets at me,
Don't please my folks too much,
Don't laugh at my jokes too much—
People will say we're in love!

Don't sigh and gaze at me,
Your sighs are so like mine,
You eyes mustn't glow like mine—
People will say we're in love!

Don't start collecting things
Give me my rose and glove;
Sweetheart, they're suspecting things—
People will say we're in love!

Verse 2 (Boy):
Some people claim that you are to blame
    as much as I.
Why do you take the trouble to bake
    my fav'rite pie?
Grantin' your wish, I carved our initials
    on the tree!
Jist keep a slice of all the advice you give
    so free.

Refrain 2:
Don't praise my charm too much,
Don't look so vain with me,
Don't stand in the rain with me—
People will say we're in love!

Don't take my arm too much,
Don't keep your hand in mine.
You hand looks so grand in mine,
People will say we're in love!

Don't dance all night with me,
Till the stars fade from above.
They'll see it's all right with me,
People will say we're in love!

The Phantom Of The Opera

Music by Andrew Lloyd Webber
Lyrics by Charles Hart
Additional Lyrics by Richard Stilgoe

from *The Phantom Of The Opera*

Christine:
In sleep he sang to me, in dreams he came,
That voice which calls to me and speaks my
   name.
And do I dream again? For now I find
The phantom of the opera is there inside my
   mind.

Phantom:
Sing once again with me our strange duet;
My power over you grows stronger yet.
And though you turn from me to glance behind,
The phantom of the opera is there inside your
   mind.

Christine:
Those who have seen your face draw back in
   fear.
I am the mask you wear,

Phantom:
It's me they fear.

Phantom & (Christine):
Your (my) spirit and my (your) voice
In one combined.
The phantom of the opera is there
Inside your (my) mind.

Voices:
He's here, the phantom of the opera.
Beware the phantom of the opera.

Phantom:
In all your fantasies, you always knew
That man and mystery were both in you.

Phantom & [Christine]:
And in this labyrinth
Where night is blind,
The phantom of the opera is there
Inside your [my] mind.

Pity The Child

Words & Music by Benny Andersson, Tim Rice & Björn Ulvaeus.

from *Chess*

When I was nine I learned survival,
Taught myself not to care.
I was my single good companion,
Taking my comfort there.
Up in my room I planned my conquests,
On my own, never asked for a helping hand;
No one would understand.
I never asked the pair who fought below,
Just in case they said no.

Pity the child who has ambition,
Knows what he wants to do.
Knows that he'll never fit the system
others expect him to.
Pity the child who knew his parents,
Saw their faults, saw their love die before his
    eyes.
Pity the child that wise.
He never asked: did I cause your distress?
Just in case they said yes.

When I was twelve my father moved out,
Left with a whimper, not with a shout.
I didn't miss him, he made it perfectly clear
I was a fool and probably queer.
Fool that I was I thought this would bring
Those he had left closer together.
She made her move the moment he crawled
    away.

I was the last the woman told,
She never let her bed get cold,
Someone moved in- I shut my door,
Someone to treat her just the same way as
    before.

I took the road of least resistance,
I had my game to play.
I had the skill, and more, the hunger, easy to
    get away.
Pity the child with no such weapons,
No defense, no escape from the ties that bind,
Always a step behind.
I never called to tell her all I'd done -
I was only her son!

Pity the child but not forever, not if he stays that
    way.
He can get all he ever wanted, if he's prepared
    to pay.
Pity instead the careless mother,
What she missed, what she lost when she let me
    go,
And I wonder, does she know?
I wouldn't call, a crazy thing to do,
Just in case she said: who?

The Point Of No Return

Music by Andrew Lloyd Webber
Words by Charles Hart
Additional Words by Richard Stilgoe

from *The Phantom Of The Opera*

Phantom (as Don Juan):
You have come here
In pursuit of your deepest urge,
In pursuit of that wish which till now
Has been silent, silent.

I have brought you
That our passions may fuse and merge,
In your mind you've already succumbed to me,
Dropped all defences,
Completely succumbed to me.
Now you are here with me,
No second thoughts,
You've decided, decided.

Past the point of no return,
No backward glances:
The games we've played till now are at an end.
Past all thought of "if" or "when",
No use resisting,
Abandon thought and let the dreams descend.

What raging fire shall flood the soul?
What rich desire unlocks its door?
What sweet seduction lies before us?

Past the point of no return,
The final threshold,
What warm unspoken secrets will we learn
Beyond the point of no return?

Christine (as Aminta):
You have brought me
To that moment where words run dry.
To that moment where speech
Disappears into silence, silence.

I have come here
Hardly knowing the reason why,
In my mind I've already imagined
Our bodies entwining,
Defenceless and silent
And now I am here with you,
No second thoughts,
I've decided, decided.

Past the point of no return,
No going back now,
Our passion play has now,
At last, begun.

Past all thought of right or wrong,
One final question:
How longs should we two wait
Before we're one?

When will the blood begin to race?
The sleeping bud burst into bloom?
When will the flames at last
Consume us?

Together:
Past the point of no return,
The final threshold,
The bridge is crossed,
So stand and watch it burn.
We've passed the point of no return.

Promises, Promises

Lyric by Hal David
Music by Burt Bacharach

from *Promises, Promises*

Promises, promises,
I'm all through with
Promises, promises now.
I don't know how
I got the nerve
To walk out.
If I shout,
Remember,
I feel free.
Now I can look at myself,
And be proud.
I'm laughing out loud,

Oh, promises, promises,
This is where those
Promises, promises end.
I won't pretend
That what was wrong
Can be right,
Ev'ry night
I'll sleep now.
No more lies.
Things that I promised myself
Fell apart,
But I found my heart.

Promises,
Their kind of promises
Can just destroy your life.
Oh, promises,
Those kind of promises
Take all the joy from life.
Oh, promises, promises,
My kind of promises
Can lead to joy,
And hope,
And love,
Yes, love!

Rainbow High

Music by Andrew Lloyd Webber
Lyrics by Tim Rice

from *Evita*

Eva:
I don't really think I need
The reasons why I won't succeed,
I have done!
Let's get this show on the road,
Let's make it obvious Peron is off and rolling

Beauticians:
Eyes! Hair! Mouth! Figure!
Dress! Voice! Style! Movement!
Hands! Magic! Rings! Glamour!
Face! Diamonds! Excitement! Image!

Eva:
I came from the people they need to adore me
So Christian Dior me from my head to my toes:
I need to be dazzling, I want to be Rainbow
   High!
They must have excitement, and so must I

Beauticians:
Eyes! Hair! Mouth! Figure!
Dress! Voice! Style! Image!

Eva:
I'm their product it's vital you sell me
So Machiavell me make me an Argentine Rose!
I need to be dazzling, I want to be Rainbow
   High!
They need their escape, and so do I.

Beauticians:
Eyes! Hair! Mouth! Figure!
Dress! Voice! Style! Image!
Style! Movement!
Hands! Magic! Rings! Glamour!
Face! Diamonds! Excitement! Image!

Eva:
All my descamisados expect me to outshine the
   enemy
The aristocracy I won't disappoint them.
I'm their saviour!
That's what they call me so Lauren Bacall me
Anything goes: to make me fantastic
I have to be Rainbow High!
In magical colours:
You're not decorating a girl for a night on the
   town!
And I'm not a second rate Queen getting kicks
   with a crown!
Next stop will be Europe! The rainbow's gonna
   tour
Dressed up somewhere to go; we'll put on a
   show!
Look out mighty Europe!
Because you oughta know what cha gonna get
   in me:
Just a little touch of,
Just a little touch of Argentina's brand of star
   quality!

Reviewing The Situation

Words & Music by Lionel Bart

from *Oliver!*

A man's got a heart, hasn't he?
Joking apart, hasn't he?
And tho' I'd be the first one to say
That I wasn't a saint,
I'm finding it hard to be really
As black as they paint.

I'm reviewing the situation.
Can a fellow be a villain all his life?
All the trials and tribulation,
Better settle down and get myself a wife.

And a wife could cook and sew for me,
And come for me and go for me,
(And go for me,)
And nag at me,
The fingers she will wag at me,
The money she will take from me,
A misery, she'll make from me,
I think I'd better think it out again.

A wife you can keep, anyway.
I'd rather sleep, anyway,
Left without anyone in the world
And I'm starting from now,
So how to win friends
And to influence people, so how?

I'm reviewing the situation.
I must quickly look up ev'ryone I know,
Titled people with a station,
Who can help me make a real
    impressive show.

I will own a suite at Claridges,
And run a fleet of carriages,
And wave at all the Duchesses
With friendliness,
As much as is befitting of my new estate.
"Good morrow to you, Magistrate!"
I think I'd better think it out again.

So, where shall I go?
Somebody?
Who do I know?
Nobody?
All my dearest companions have
Always been villains and thieves—
So at my time of life I should
Start turning over new leaves.

I'm reviewing the situation.
If you want to eat you've got to earn a bob!
Is it such a humiliation
For a robber to perform an honest job?

So a job I'm getting possibly,
I wonder how the boss'll be?
I wonder if he'll take to me?
What bonuses he'll make to me?
I'll start at eight, and finish late,
At normal rate and all, but wait!
I think I'd better think it out again.

What happens if I'm seventy?
Must come a time—seventy,
When you're old and it's cold
And who cares if you live or you die.
Your one consolation's
The money you may have put by.

I'm reviewing the situation,
I'm a bad 'un and a bad 'un I shall stay!
You'll be seeing no transformation,
But it's wrong to be a rogue in ev'ryway.

I don't want nobody hurt for me,
Or made to do the dirt for me.
This rotten life is not for me.
It's getting far too hot for me.
Don't want no one to rob for me,
But who will find a job for me?
I don't care what they've got for me.
But who will change the plot for me?
I think I'll have to think it out again.
Hey!

The Rhythm Of Life

Music by Cy Coleman
Lyrics by Dorothy Fields

from *Sweet Charity*

Daddy started out in San Francisco,
Tootin' on a trumpet loud and mean,
Suddenly a voice said, "Go forth Daddy,
Spread the picture on a wider screen."
And the voice said, "Brother, there's a million
    pigeons
Ready to be hooked on new religions.
Hit the road, Daddy, leave you common-law
    wife,
Spread the religion of The Rhythm of Life."

And The Rhythm of Life is a powerful beat,
Puts a tingle in your fingers and a tingle in your
    feet,
Rhythm in your bedroom, rhythm in the street,
Yes, The Rhythm of Life is a powerful beat.
To feel The Rhythm of Life, to feel the powerful
    beat,
To feel the tingle in your fingers, to feel the
    tingle in your feet.

Daddy spread the gospel in Milwaukee,
Took his walkie talkie to Rocky Ridge,
Blew his way to Canton, then to Scranton,
Till he landed under the Manhattan Bridge.
Daddy was a new sensation,
Got himself a congregation,
Built up quite an operation down below.
With the pie-eyed piper blowing,
While the muscatel was flowing,
All the cats were go, go, going down below.

Daddy was a new sensation,
Got himself a congregation,
Built up quite an operation down below.
With the pie-eyed piper blowing,
While the muscatel was flowing,
All the cats were go, go, going down below.

Flip your wings and fly to Daddy,
Flip your wings and fly to Daddy,
Flip your wings and fly to Daddy,
Fly, fly, fly to Daddy.

Hit the floor and crawl to Daddy,
Hit the floor and crawl to Daddy,
Hit the floor and crawl to Daddy,
Crawl, crawl, crawl to Daddy.

To The Rhythm of Life, to feel the powerful
    beat,
To feel the rhythm in your fingers,
To feel the tingle in your feet.
To The Rhythm of Life, to feel the powerful
    beat,
To feel the rhythm in your fingers,
To feel the tingle in your feet.

Flip your wings and fly to Daddy,
Take a dive and swim to Daddy,
Hit the floor and crawl to Daddy,
Daddy we got The Rhythm of Life, of life, of life,
    of life.
Yeah! Yeah! Yeah! Man!

River In The Rain

Words & Music by Roger Miller

from *Big River*

Refrain 1:
River in the rain,
Sometimes at night you look like a long white
    train,
Windin' your way, away somewhere.
River, I love you,
Don't you care?

If you're on the run,
Windin' someplace just tryin' to find the sun.
Whether the sunshine, whether the rain,
River, I love you, just the same.

Refrain 2:
But sometimes in a time of trouble,
When you're out of hand and your muddy
    bubbles
Roll across my floor,
Carryin' way the things I treasure;
Hell, there ain't no way to measure
Why I love you more
Than I did the day before.

Refrain 1

Refrain 2

River in the rain,
Sometimes at night you look like a long white
    train,
Windin' your way away from me.
River, I've never seen the sea.

The Road You Didn't Take

Words & Music by Stephen Sondheim

from *Follies*

You're either a poet or you're a lover,
Or you're the famous Benjamin Stone.
You take one road,
You try one door,
There isn't time for any more.
One's life consists of either/or.
One has regrets which one forgets,
And as the years go on,

The road you didn't take hardly comes to mind,
Does it?
The door you didn't try,
Where could it have led?
The choice you didn't make never was defined,
Was it?
Dreams you didn't dare are dead.
Were they ever there?
Who said?
I don't remember,
I don't remember at all.

The books I'll never read wouldn't change a
    thing,
Would they?
The girls I'll never know,
I'm too tired for.
The lives I'll never lead couldn't make me sing,
Could they?
Could they?
Could they?
Chances that you miss,
Ignore.
Ignorance is bliss;
What's more, you won't remember,
You won't remember at all,
Not at all.

ou yearn for the women,
Long for the money,
Envy the famous Benjamin Stones.
You take your road,
The decades fly,
The yearnings fade, the longings die.
You learn to bid them all goodbye.
And oh, the peace, the blessed peace.
At last you come to know.

The roads you never take go through rocky
    ground,
Don't they?
The choices that you make aren't all that grim.
The worlds you never see still will be around,
Won't they?
The Ben I'll never be,
Who remembers him?

S.O.S.

Words & Music by Benny Andersson, Björn Ulvaeus & Stig Anderson

from *Mamma Mia!*

Sam:
Where are those happy days?
They seem so hard to find.
I try to reach for you
But you have closed your mind.

Whatever happened to our love?
I wish I understood.
It used to be so nice
It used to be so good.

So when you're near me
Darling, can't you hear me? S.O.S.
The love you gave me
Nothing else can save me. S.O.S
When you're gone
How can I even try to go on?
When you're gone
Though I try, how can I carry on?

Donna:
You seem so very far away
Though you are standing near.
You made me feel alive
But something died I fear.

I really tried to make it out.
I wish I understood.
What happened to our love?
It used to be so good.

Donna/Sam:
So when you're near me
Darling, can't you hear me? S.O.S.
The love you gave me
Nothing else can save me. S.O.S
When you're gone
How can I even try to go on?
When you're gone
Though I try, how can I carry on?

So when you're near me
Darling, can't you hear me? S.O.S.
The love you gave me
Nothing else can save me. S.O.S
When you're gone
How can I even try to go on?
When you're gone
Though I try, how can I carry on?

Satin Doll

Words by Johnny Mercer & Billy Strayhorn
Music by Duke Ellington

from *Sophisticated Ladies*

Cigarette holder
Which wigs me
Over her shoulder,
She digs me
Out cattin' that satin doll.

Baby shall we go
Out skippin'
Careful amigo,
You're flippin'
Speaks Latin that satin doll.

She's nobody's fool,
So I'm playing it cool as can be,
I'll give it a whirl,
But I ain't for no girl catching me.

Spoken:
Switch-E-Rooney

Sung:
Telephone numbers well you know,
Doing my rhumbas with uno,
And that 'n' my satin doll.

Seasons Of Love

Words & Music by Jonathan Larson

from *Rent*

Five hundred twenty-five thousand
 six hundred minutes,
Five hundred twenty-five thousand
 moments so dear.
Five hundred twenty-five thousand
 six hundred minutes.
How do you measure, measure a year?

In daylights, in sunsets,
In midnights, in cups of coffee,
In inches, in miles, in laughter, in strife,
In five hundred twenty-five thousand
 six hundred minutes.
How do you measure a year in the life.

How about love?
How about love?
How about love?
Measure in love.
Seasons of love,
Seasons of love.

Five hundred twenty-five thousand
 six hundred minutes,
Five hundred twenty-five thousand
 journeys to plan.
Five hundred twenty-five thousand
 six hundred minutes.
How do you measure the life of a woman or a
 man?

In truth that she learned,
Or in times that he cried,
In bridges he burned,
Or the way that she died.
It's time now to sing out,
Though the story never ends.
Let's celebrate, remember,
A year in the life of friends.

Remember the love,
Remember the love,
Remember the love,
Measure in love,
Seasons of love,
Seasons of love.

Second Hand Rose

Words by Grant Clarke
Music by James F. Hanley

from *Ziegfeld Follies Of 1921*

Father has a business,
Strictly second hand,
Everything from toothpicks
To a baby grand.
Stuff in our apartment
Came from father's store.
Even clothes I'm wearing,
Someone wore before.
It's no wonder
That I feel abused.
I never get a thing
That ain't been used.

I'm wearing second hand hats, second hand
   clothes,
That's why they call me second hand Rose.
Even our piano in the parlor,
Father bought for ten cents on the dollar.
Second hand pearls,
I'm wearing second hand curls.
I never get a single thing that's new.
Even Jake the plumber, he's the man I adore,
Had the nerve to tell me he's been married
   before.
Everyone knows that I'm just second hand
   Rose,
From Second Avenue.

I'm wearing second hand shoes, second hand
   hose,
All the girls hand me their second hand beaux.
Even my pajamas when I don 'em
Have somebody else's initials on 'em.
Second hand rings, I'm sick of second hand
   things.
I never get what other girlies do.
Once while strolling through the Ritz
A girl got my goat,
She nudged her friend and said,
"Ooh look, here's my old fur coat."
Everyone knows that I'm just Second Hand
   Rose,
From Second Avenue.

Seventy Six Trombones

Words & Music by Meredith Willson

from *The Music Man*

Seventy six trombones led the big parade,
With a hundred and ten cornets close at hand.
They were followed by rows and rows of the
    finest virtuosos,
The cream of ev'ry famous band.

Seventy six trombones caught the morning sun,
With a hundred and ten cornets right behind.
There were more than a thousand reeds
    springing up like weeds,
There were horns of ev'ry shape and kind.

There were copper bottom timpani in horse
    platoons,
Thundering, thundering, all along the way.
Double bell euphoniums and big bassoons,
Each bassoon having his big fat say.
There were fifty mounted cannon in the battery,
Thundering, thundering, louder than before.
Clarinets of ev'ry size and trumpeters who'd
    improvise
A full octave higher than the score.

Seventy six trombones hit the counterpoint,
While a hundred and ten cornets blazed away.
To the rhythm of Harch! Harch! Harch!
All the kids began to march,
And they're marching still right today.

Shall We Dance?

Lyrics by Oscar Hammerstein II
Music by Richard Rodgers

from *The King & I*

We've just been introduced,
I do not know you well,
But when the music started,
Something drew me to your side.
So many men and girls are in each other's
    arms,
It made me think we might be
Similarly occupied.

Refrain:
Shall we dance?
On a bright cloud of music shall we fly?
Shall we dance?
Shall we then say "Good night" and mean
    "Good bye"?
Or, perchance,
When the last little star has left the sky,
Shall we still be together
With our arms around each other
And shall you be my new romance?
On the clear understanding
That this kind of thing can happen,
Shall we dance?
Shall we dance?
Shall we dance?

Sing for Your Supper

Words by Lorenz Hart
Music by Richard Rodgers

from *The Boys From Syracuse*

Hawks and crows do lots of things,
But the canary only sings.
She is a courtesan on wings,
So I've heard.
Eagles and storks are twice as strong.
All the canary knows is a song.
But the canary gets along,
Gilded bird!

Sing for your supper,
And you'll get breakfast.
Songbirds always eat
If their song is sweet to hear.
Sing for your luncheon,
And you'll get dinner.
Dine with wine of choice,
If romance is in your voice.
I heard from a wise canary
Trilling makes a fellow willing,
So, little swallow, swallow now.
Now is the time to
Sing for your supper,
And you'll get breakfast.
Songbirds are not dumb,
They don't buy a crumb
Of bread,
It's said.
So sing and you'll be fed.

Sit Down You're Rockin' The Boat

Words & Music by Frank Loesser

from *Guys & Dolls*

I dreamed last night I got on the boat to heaven
And by some chance I had brought my dice
   along.
And there I stood and I hollered, "Someone
   fade me,"
But the passengers they knew right from wrong.

For the people all said, "Sit down,
Sit down, you're rockin' the boat;
And the devil will drag you under
By the sharp lapel of your checkered coat;
Sit down, sit down, sit down, sit down,
Sit down, you're rockin' the boat.

I sailed away on that little boat to heaven
And by some chance found a bottle in my fist.
And there I stood nicely passin' out the whiskey,
But the passengers were bound to resist.

For all the people said, "Beware,
Beware you'll scuttle the ship;
And the devil will drag you under
By the fancy tie 'round your wicked throat;
Sit down, sit down, sit down, sit down,
Sit down, you're rockin' the boat.

And as I laughed at those passengers to heaven
A great big wave came and washed me
   overboard.
And as I sank, and I hollered, "Someone save
   me,"
That's the moment I woke up, thank the Lord.

And I said to myself, "Sit down,
Sit down, you're rockin' the boat."
Said to myself, "Sit down, you're rockin' the
   boat."
And the devil will drag you under
With a soul so heavy you'd never float;
Sit down, sit down, sit down, sit down,
Sit down, you're rockin' the boat.

Smoke Gets In Your Eyes

Music by Jerome Kern
Lyrics by Otto Harbach

from *Roberta*

They asked me how I knew
My true love was true.
I of course replied,
Something here inside
Cannot be denied.

They said some day you'll find
All who love are blind,
When your heart's on fire,
You must realize
Smoke gets in your eyes.

So I chaffed them and I gaily laughed
To think they could doubt my love.
Yet today my love has flown away
I am without my love.

Now laughing friends deride
Tears I cannot hide.
So I smile and say
When a lovely flame dies
Smoke gets in your eyes.

Sixteen Going On Seventeen

Lyrics by Oscar Hammerstein II
Music by Richard Rodgers

from *The Sound Of Music*

You wait, little girl, on an empty stage
For fate to turn the light on.
Your life, little girl, is an empty page
That men will want to write on,
To write on.

You are sixteen, going on seventeen,
Baby, it's time to think.
Better beware,
Be canny and careful,
Baby, you're on the brink.

You are sixteen, going on seventeen,
Fellows will fall in line,
Eager young lads
And roués and cads
Will offer you food and wine.

Totally unprepared are you
To face a world of men.
Timid and shy and scared are you
Of things beyond your ken.

You need someone older and wiser
Telling you what to do...
I am seventeen, going on eighteen,
I'll take care of you.

I am sixteen, going on seventeen,
I know that I'm naïve.
Fellows I meet
May tell me I'm sweet
And willingly I'll believe.

I am sixteen, going on seventeen,
Innocent as a rose.
Bachelor dandies,
Drinkers of brandies,
What do I know of those?

Totally unprepared am I
To face a world of men,
Timid and shy and scared am I
Of things beyond my ken.

I need someone older and wiser
Telling me what to do...
You are seventeen, going on eighteen,
I'll depend on you.

A bell is no bell till you ring it,
A song is no song till you sing it,
And love in your heart
Wasn't put there to stay,
Love isn't love
Till you give it away.

When you're sixteen, going on seventeen,
Waiting for life to start,
Somebody kind
Who touches your mind
Will suddenly touch your heart!

When that happens, after it happens,
Nothing is quite the same.
Somehow you know
You'll jump up and go
If ever he calls your name!

Gone are your old ideas of life,
The old ideas grow dim—
Lo and behold! You're someone's wife
And you belong to him!

You may think this kind of adventure
Never may come to you...
Darling sixteen-going-on-seventeen,
Wait a year or two.

Gone are your old ideas of life,
The old ideas grow dim
Lo and behold! You're someone's wife
And you belong to him!

You may think this kind of adventure
Never may come to you...
Darling sixteen-going-on-seventeen,
Wait a year or two.

Some Enchanted Evening

Lyrics by Oscar Hammerstein II
Music by Richard Rodgers

from *South Pacific*

Some enchanted evening
You may see a stranger,
You may see a stranger
Across a crowded room.
And somehow you know,
You know even then,
That somewhere you'll see her again
    and again.

Some enchanted evening
Someone may be laughing,
You may hear her laughing
Across a crowded room—
And night after night,
As strange as it seems,
The sound of her laughter will sing in
    your dreams.

Who can explain it?
Who can tell you why?
Fools give you reasons—
Wise men never try.

Some enchanted evening
When you find your true love,
When you hear her call you
Across a crowded room,
Then fly to her side
And make her your own,
Or all through your life
You may dream all alone.
Once you have found her,
Never let her go.
Once you have found her,
Never let her go.

Somebody, Somewhere

Words & Music by Frank Loesser

from *The Most Happy Fella*

Wanting to be wanted,
Needing to be needed,
That's what it is.
That's what it is.
Now I'm lucky that:

Somebody, somewhere
Wants me and needs me,
That's very wonderful
To know.

Somebody lonely
Wants me to care,
Wants me of all people
To notice him there.

Well, I want to be wanted,
Need to be needed,
And I'll admit I'm all
Aglow.

'Cause somebody, somewhere
Wants me and needs me,
Wants lonely me to smile
And say, "Hello."

Somebody, somewhere
Wants me and needs me,
And that's very wonderful
To know.

Someone Like You

Words by Leslie Bricusse
Music by Frank Wildhorn

from *Jekyll & Hyde*

I peered through the windows, watched life go
    by
Dreamed of tomorrow, but stayed inside.
The past was holding me, keeping life at bay.
I wandered, lost in yesterday,
Wanting to fly, but scared to try.

Then someone like you found someone like
    me.
And suddenly nothing is the same.
My heart's taken wing, I feel so alive,
'Cause someone like you found me.

It's like you took my dreams, made each one
    real,
You reached inside of me and made me feel.
And now I see a world I've never seen before.
Your love has opened every door;
You've set me free, now I can soar.

For someone like you found someone like me.
You touched my heart, nothing is the same.
There's a new way to live, a new way to love,
'Cause someone like you found me.

Oh, someone like you found someone like me.
And suddenly nothing will ever be the same.
My heart's taken wing, and I feel so alive,
'Cause someone like you loves me,
Loves me.

Someone Nice Like You

Words & Music by Leslie Bricusse & Anthony Newley

from *Stop The World—I Want To Get Off*

Why did someone nice like you, Evie
    [sweetheart],
Have to love someone like me?
When I think of all the men you could have
    loved,
The men you should have loved,
Who would have loved you,
You're worth so much more than me, Evie
    [sweetheart].
Believe you me, Evie [sweetheart],
You know that's true.
And if we could live twice,
I'd make life paradise,
For someone really nice like you.

You ask, why did someone nice like me
Have to love someone like you?
And you mention all the men I could have
    loved,
The men I should have loved,
Who would have loved me,
Maybe Sigmund Freud could tell you why
I'll love you till I die,
The way I do.
But who wants Freud's advice?
I'm sure it works with mice,
But not with someone nice like you.

Something Wonderful

Lyrics by Oscar Hammerstein II
Music by Richard Rodgers

from *The King & I*

This is a man who thinks with his heart,
His heart is not always wise.
This is a man who stumbles and falls,
But this is a man who tries.
This is a man you'll forgive and forgive,
And help and protect, as long as you live...

He will not always say
What you would have him say,
But now and then he'll say
Something wonderful.

The thoughtless things he'll do
Will hurt and worry you,
But now and then he'll do
Something wonderful.

He has a thousand dreams
That won't come true.
You know that he believes in them
And that's enough for you.
You'll always go along,
Defend him when he's wrong
And tell him, when he's strong
He is wonderful.
He'll always need your love,
And so he'll get your love,
A man who needs your love
Can be wonderful!

Sophisticated Lady

Words & Music by Duke Ellington, Irving Mills & Mitchell Parish

from *Sophisticated Ladies*

They say into your early life romance came
And this heart of yours burned a flame,
A flame that flickered one day
And died away.
Then, with disillusion deep in your eyes
You learned that fools in love soon grow wise.

The years have changed you, somehow
I see you now…
Smoking, drinking,
Never thinking of tomorrow,
Nonchalant.
Diamonds shining,
Dancing, dining
With some man in a restaurant.
Is that all you really want?
No, sophisticated lady,
I know
You miss the love you lost long ago,
And when nobody is nigh
You cry.

Sorry-Grateful

Words & Music by Stephen Sondheim

from *Company*

You're always sorry,
You're always grateful,
You're always wond'ring
What might have been.
Then she walks in.

And still you're sorry,
And still you're grateful,
And still you wonder,
And still you doubt,
And she goes out.

Ev'rything's diff'rent,
Nothing's changed,
Only maybe slightly
Rearranged.

Refrain:
You're sorry-grateful,
Regretful-happy.
Why look for answers
Where none occur?

You always are
What you always were,
Which has nothing to do with,
All to do with her.

You're always sorry,
You're always grateful,
You hold her, thinking,
"I'm not alone."
You're still alone.

You don't live for her,
You do live with her.
You're scared she's starting
To drift away,
And scared she'll stay.

Good things get better,
Bad get worse.
Wait, I think I meant that
In reverse.

Refrain

You'll always be
What you always were,
Which has nothing to do with,
All to do with her.

The Sound Of Music

Lyrics by Oscar Hammerstein II
Music by Richard Rodgers

from *The Sound Of Music*

My day in the hills has come to an end, I know.
A star has come out to tell me it's time to go,
But deep in the dark-green shadows
Are voices that urge me to stay.
So I pause and I wait and I listen
For one more sound,
For one more lovely thing
That the hills might say...

The hills are alive
With the sound of music,
With songs they have sung
For a thousand years.
The hills fill my heart
With the sound of music—
My heart wants to sing
Every song it hears.

My heart wants to beat
Like the wings of the birds that rise
From the lake to the trees.
My heart wants to sigh like a chime that flies
From a church on a breeze,
To laugh like a brook when it trips and falls
Over stones in its way,
To sing through the night
Like a lark that is learning to pray—

I go to the hills when my heart is lonely,
I know I will hear what I've heard before.
My heart will be blessed with the sound of
    music
And I'll sing once more.

Springtime For Hitler

Words & Music by Mel Brooks

from *The Producers*

Germany was having trouble,
What a sad, sad story,
Needed a new leader to restore its former glory.
Where, oh where, was he?
Where could that man be?
We looked around and then we found
The man for you and me.

And now it's springtime for Hitler and Germany,
Deutschland is happy and gay,
We're marching to a faster pace,
Look out, here comes the master race.
Springtime for Hitler and Germany,
Rhineland's a fine land once more.
Springtime for Hitler and Germany,
Look out Europe, we're goin' on tour.

Springtime for Hitler and Germany,
Winter for Poland and France.
Springtime for Hitler and Germany,
Come on Germans, go into your dance!

Spoken:
I was born in Düsseldorf,
And that is why they call me Rolf.
Don't be stupid, be a smarty,
Come and join the Nazi party.

Sung:
And now it's springtime for Hitler and Germany,
Goosesteps, the new step today.
Bombs falling from the skies again,
Deutschland is on the rise again.

Springtime for Hitler and Germany,
U-boats are sailing once more.
Springtime for Hitler and Germany
Means that soon we'll be going,
We've got to be going,
You know we'll be going,
You bet we'll be going,
You know we'll be going to war!

Starlight Express

Music by Andrew Lloyd Webber
Lyrics by Richard Stilgoe

from *Starlight Express*

When your good nights have been said
And you are lying in bed
With the covers pulled up tight
And though you count every sheep
You get the feeling that sleep
Is gonna stay away tonight.
That's when you hear it coming
That is when you hear the humming of the

Starlight Express, Starlight Express
Are you real? Yes or no?
Starlight Express, answer me yes,
I don't want you to go.

Want you to take me away
But bring me home before daylight
And in the time between
Take me to everywhere
But don't abandon me there
Just want to say I've been.
I believe in you completely
Though I may be dreaming sweetly of the

Starlight Express, Starlight Express,
Are you real? Yes or no?
Starlight Express, answer me yes,
I don't want you to go.

And if you're there
And if you know
Then show me which way I should go!

Starlight Express, Starlight Express,
Are you real? Yes or no?
Starlight Express, answer me yes,
I don't want you to go.

Starlight Express, Starlight Express,
Are you real? Are you near?
Starlight Express, answer me yes,
I need you to be here.

Stars

Music by Claude-Michel Schönberg
Lyrics by Alain Boublil & Herbert Kretzmer

from *Les Misérables*

There, out in the darkness,
A fugitive running,
Fallen from grace,
Fallen from grace.
God be my witness,
I never shall yield,
Till we come face to face,
Till we come face to face.

He knows his way in the dark,
But mine is the way of the Lord.
And those who follow the path
Of the righteous shall have their reward.
And if they fall, as Lucifer fell,
The flame, the sword!

Stars, in your multitudes,
Scarce to be counted,
Filling the darkness,
With order and light.
You are the sentinels,
Silent and sure,
Keeping watch in the night,
Keeping watch in the night.

You know your place in the skies,
You hold your course and your aim.
And each in your season returns and returns,
And is always the same.
And if you fall, as Lucifer fell,
You fall in flame!

And so it has been,
And so it is written
On the doorways to paradise,
That those who falter
And those who fall
Must pay the price.

Lord, let me find him,
That I may see him,
Safe behind bars!
I will never rest 'til then.
This I swear!
This I swear by the stars.

Stepsisters' Lament

Lyrics by Oscar Hammerstein II
Music by Richard Rodgers

from *Cinderella*

Why would a fellow want a girl like her,
A frail and fluffy beauty?
Why can't a fellow ever once prefer
A solid girl like me?

She's a frothy little bubble
With a flimsy kind of charm,
And with very little trouble,
I could break her little arm!

Oh, oh, why would a fellow want a girl like her,
So obviously unusual?
Why can't a fellow ever once prefer
A usual girl like me?

Her cheeks are a pretty shade of pink,
But not any pinker than a rose is.
Her skin may be delicate and soft,
But not any softer than a doe's is.

Her neck is no whiter than a swan's.
She's only as dainty as a daisy.
She's only as graceful as a bird.
So why is the fellow going crazy?

Oh, why would a fellow want a girl like her,
A girl who's merely lovely?
Why can't a fellow ever once prefer
A girl who's merely me?
What's the matter with the man?
What's the matter with the man?
What's the matter with the man?

Summer Nights

Words & Music by Warren Casey & Jim Jacobs

from *Grease*

Boy: Summer lovin' had me blast.
Girl: Summer lovin' happened so fast.
Boy: Met a girl crazy for me.
Girl: Met a boy, cute as can be.

Summer days drifting away
To, uh, oh, those summer nights.

Well-a, well-a, well-a
Tell me more. Tell me more.
Did you get very far?
Tell me more. Tell me more.
Like, does he have a car?

Boy: She swam by me. She got a cramp.
Girl: He ran by me, got my suit damp.
Boy: Saved her life, she nearly drowned.
Girl: He showed of, splashing around.

Summer sun, something's begun
But, uh, oh, those summer nights.

Well-a, well-a, well-a uh.
Tell me more. Tell me more.
Was it love at first sight?
Tell me more. Tell me more.
Did she put up a fight?

Boy: Took her bowling in the arcade.
Girl: We went strolling; drank lemonade.
Boy: We made out under the dock.
Girl: We stayed out till ten o'clock.

Summer fling don't mean a thing
But uh, oh, those summer nights.

Tell me more, tell me more.
But you don't got to brag.
Tell me more, tell me more.
'Cause he sounds like a drag.
Shu-da bop bop. Shu-da bop bop.
Shu-da bop bop. Shu-da bop bop.

Girl: He got friendly, holding my hand.
Boy: She got friendly, down in the sand.
Girl: He was sweet; just turned eighteen.
Boy: She was good. You know what I mean.

Summer heat; boy and girl meet.
But, uh, oh those summer nights.

Tell me more. Tell me more.
How much dough did he spend?
Tell me more. Tell me more.
Could she get me a friend?

Girl: It turned colder; that's where it ends.
Boy: So I told her we'd still be friends.
Girl: Then we made our true love vow.
Boy: Wonder what she's doin' now.

Summer dreams
Ripped at the seams
But, oh, those summer nights.
Tell me more.
Tell me more.

Sun And Moon

Music by Claude-Michel Schönberg
Lyrics by Richard Maltby Jr. & Alain Boublil
Adapted from original French Lyrics by Alain Boublil

from *Miss Saigon*

You are sunlight and I moon,
Joined by the gods of fortune,
Midnight and high noon,
Sharing the sky.
We have been blessed, you and I.

You are here like a myst'ry.
I'm from a world that's so diff'rent
From all that you are.
How in the light of one night
Did we come so far?

Outside, day starts to dawn.
Your moon still floats on high.
The birds awake.
The stars shine, too.
My hands still shake,
I reach for you,
And we meet in the sky.

You are sunlight and I moon,
Joined here bright'ning the sky
With the flame of love.
Made of sunlight, moonlight.

Superstar

Music by Andrew Lloyd Webber
Lyrics by Tim Rice

from *Jesus Christ Superstar*

Voice of Judas:
Ev'ry time I look at you I don't understand
Why you let the things you did get so out of
hand.
You'd have managed better if you'd had it
planned.
Why'd you choose such a backward time and
such a strange land?
If you'd come today you would have reached a
whole nation
Israel in 4 BC had no mass communication

Choir:
Don't you get me wrong

Voice of Judas:
Don't you get me wrong

Choir:
Don't you get me wrong now

Voice of Judas:
Don't you get me wrong

Choir:
Don't you get me wrong

Voice of Judas:
Don't you get me wrong

Choir:
Don't you get me wrong

Voice of Judas:
Don't you get me wrong now

Choir:
I only want to know

Voice of Judas:
Only want to know

Choir:
I only want to know now

Voice of Judas:
Only want to know

Choir:
I only want to know

Voice of Judas:
Only want to know

Choir:
I only want to know

Voice of Judas:
Only want to know

Choir:
Jesus Christ Jesus Christ
Who are you? What have you sacrificed?
Jesus Christ Jesus Christ
Who are you? What have you sacrificed?
Jesus Christ Superstar
Do you think you're what they say you are?
Jesus Christ Superstar
Do you think you're what they say you are?

Voice of Judas:
Tell me what you think about your friends at the
top
Who d'you think besides yourself's the pick of
the crop?
Buddah was he where it's at? Is he where you
are?
Could Mahomet move a mountain or was that
just PR?
Did you mean to die like that? Was that a
mistake
Or did you know you messy death would be a
record breaker?

Choir:
Don't you get me wrong

Voice of Judas:
Don't you get me wrong

Choir:
Don't you get me wrong now

Voice of Judas:
Don't you get me wrong

Choir:
Don't you get me wrong

Voice of Judas:
Don't you get me wrong

Choir:
Don't you get me wrong

Voice of Judas:
Don't you get me wrong now

Choir:
I only want to know

Voice of Judas:
Only want to know

Choir:
I only want to know now

Voice of Judas:
Only want to know

Choir:
I only want to know

Voice of Judas:
Only want to know

Choir:
I only want to know

Voice of Judas:
Only want to know

Choir:
Jesus Christ Jesus Christ
Who are you? What have you sacrificed?
Jesus Christ Jesus Christ
Who are you? What have you sacrificed?
Jesus Christ Superstar
Do you think you're what they say you are?
Jesus Christ Superstar
Do you think you're what they say you are?
Jesus Christ Superstar
Do you think you're what they say you are?
(Repeat and fade)

Super Trouper

Words & Music by Benny Andersson & Björn Ulvaeus

from *Mamma Mia!*

Donna & The Dynamos:
Super Trouper
Beams are gonna blind me
But I won't feel blue
Like I always do
'Cause somewhere in the crowd there's you.

Donna:
I was sick and tired of everything
When I called you last night from Glasgow.
All I do is eat and sing,
Wishing every show was the last show

So imagine I was glad to hear you're coming
Suddenly it all feels right.
And it's gonna be so different when I'm on the
    stage tonight.

Donna & The Dynamos (Refrain):
Tonight the Super Trouper
lights are gonna find me
Shining like the sun
Smiling having fun
Feeling like a number one.
Tonight the Super Trouper
beams are gonna blind me
But I won't feel blue
Like I always do.
'Cause somewhere in the crowd there's you.

Donna:
Facing twenty thousand of your friends
How can anyone be so lonely?
Part of a success that never ends,
Still I'm thinking about you only.

There are moments when I think I'm going
    crazy
But it's gonna be alright.
And it's gonna be so different when I'm on the
    stage tonight.

Refrain

Donna:
So I'll be there
When you arrive
The sight of you
Will prove to me
I'm still alive
And when you take me in your arms
And hold me tight
I know it's gonna mean
So much tonight.

Refrain

The Surrey With The Fringe On Top

Lyrics by Oscar Hammerstein II
Music by Richard Rodgers

from *Oklahoma!*

When I take you out tonight with me,
Honey, here's the way it's goin' to be:
You will set behind a team of snow-white
 horses
In the slickest gig you ever see!

Chicks and ducks and geese better scurry
When I take you out in the surrey,
When I take you out in the surrey with the
 fringe on top.
Watch that fringe and see how it flutters
When I drive them high-steppin' strutters
Nosey-pokes'll peek through their shutters
And their eyes will pop!
The wheels are yeller, the upholstery's brown,
The dashboard's genuine leather,
With isinglass curtains you can roll right down
In case there's a change in the weather;
Two bright side lights winkin' and blinkin',
Aint no finer rig, I'm a-thinkin';
You c'n keep yer rig if you're thinkin' 'at I'd
 keer to swap
Fer that shiny little surrey with the fringe on the
 top.

Would y' say the fringe was made of silk?
Wouldn't have no other kind but silk.
Has it really got a team of snow-white horses?
One's like snow—the other's more like milk

All the world'll fly in a flurry
When I take you out in the surrey,
When I take you out in the surrey with the
 fringe on top.

When we hit the road, hell for leather,
Cats and dogs'll dance in the heather,
Birds and frogs'll sing altogether,
And the toads will hop!
The wind'll whistle as we rattle along,
The cows'll moo in the clover,
The river will ripple out a whispered song,
And whisper it over and over:
Don't you wisht y'd go on ferever?
Don't you wisht y'd go on ferever?
Don't you wisht y'd go on ferever and ud never
 stop
In that shiny little surrey with the fringe on the
 top?

I can see the stars gittin' blurry
When we ride back home in the surrey,
Drivin' slowly home in the surrey with the
 fringe on top.
I can feel the day gittin' older,
Feel a sleepy head near my shoulder,
Noddin', droopin' close to my shoulder till it
 falls, kerplop!
The sun is swimmin' on the rim of a hill,
The moon is takin' a header,
And jist as I'm thinkin' all the earth is still,
A lark'll wake up in the medder…
Hush! You bird, my baby's a-sleepin'—
Maybe got a dream worth a-keepin'.
Whoa! You team, and jist keep a-creepin' at a
 slow clip-clop;
Don't you hurry with the surrey with the fringe
 on the top.

The Sweetest Sounds

Words & Music by Richard Rodgers

from *No Strings*

What do I really hear?
What is in the ear of my mind?
Which sounds are true and clear,
And which will never be defined?

The sweetest sounds I'll ever hear
Are still inside my head.
The kindest words I'll ever know
Are waiting to be said.
The most entrancing sight of all
Is yet for me to see.
And the dearest love in all the world
Is waiting somewhere for me.
Is waiting somewhere,
Somewhere for me.

Take Back Your Mink

Words & Music by Frank Loesser

from *Guys & Dolls*

He gave me the fur coat five winters ago
And the gown the following fall
Then the bracelet, the bag, the hat and the
   shoes
That was late 'forty eight, I recall.
Then last night in his apartment he tried to
   remove them all
And I said as I ran down the hall:

Take back your mink take back your pearls
What made you think that I was one of those
   girls (I'm screamin')
Take back the gown the gloves and the hat
I may be down but I'm not flat as all that.

I thot that each expensive gift you'd arrange
Was a token of your esteem
Now when I think of what you want in
   exchange,
It all seems a horrible dream;

So take back your mink those old worn- out
   pelts
And go shorten the sleeves for somebody else!

Take back your mink take back your pearls
What made you think that I was one of those
   girls (I'm screamin')
Take back the gown the gloves and the hat
I may be down but I'm not flat as all that.

I thot that each expensive gift you'd arrange
Was a token of your esteem
Now when I think of what you want in
   exchange,
It all seems a horrible dream;

So take back your mink to from whence it
   came
And tell 'em to Hollanderize it for some other
   dame!

Tell Me On A Sunday

Music by Andrew Lloyd Webber
Lyrics by Don Black

from *Song & Dance*

Don't write a letter when you want to leave.
Don't call me at 3 A.M. from a friend's
    apartment.
I'd like to choose
How I hear the news.
Take me to a park that's covered with trees.
Tell me on a Sunday, please.

Let me down easy, no big song and dance.
No long faces, no long looks, no deep
    conversation.
I know the way
We should spend the day.
Take me to a zoo that's got chimpanzees.
Tell me on a Sunday, please.

Don't want to know who's to blame,
It won't help knowing.
Don't want to fight
Day and night,
Bad enough you're going.

Don't leave me in silence with no words
    at all.
Don't get drunk and slam the door,
That's no way to end this.
I know how I want to say goodbye.
Find a circus ring with a flying trapeze.
Tell me on a Sunday, please.
I don't want to fight day and night,
Bad enough you're going.

Don't leave in silence with no words at all.
Don't get drunk and slam the door,
That's no way to end this.
I know how I want you to say goodbye.
Don't run off in the pouring rain.
Don't call me as they call your plane.
Take the hurt out of all the pain.
Take me to a park that's covered with trees.
Tell me on a Sunday, please.

Thank Heaven For Little Girls

Words by Alan Jay Lerner
Music by Frederick Loewe

from *Gigi*

Each time I see a little girl,
Of five, or six, or seven,
I can't resist a joyous urge
To smile and say:

Thank heaven for little girls!
For little girls get bigger ev'ry day.
Thank heaven for little girls!
They grow up in the most delightful way.

Those little eyes,
So helpless and appealing,
One day will flash,
And send you crashing through the ceiling.

Thank heaven for little girls.
Thank heaven for them all,
No matter where,
No matter who,
Without them what would little boys do?
Thank heaven,
Thank heaven.
Thank heaven for little girls.

Thank You For The Music

Words & Music by Benny Andersson & Björn Ulvaeus

from *Mamma Mia!*

Harry:

Thank you for the music, the songs I'm singing,
Thanks for all the joy they're bringing.
Who can live without it?
I ask in all honesty;
What would life be?

Harry/Sophie:

Without a song or a dance, what are we?
So I say thank you for the music,
For giving it to me.

Sophie:

Mother says I was a dancer before I could
    walk.
She says I began to sing long before I could
    talk.
And I've often wondered, how did it all start?
Who found out that nothing can capture a heart
Like a melody can?
Well, whoever it was, I'm a fan.

Sophie/Harry:

So I say,
Thank you for the music, the songs I'm singing,
Thanks for all the joy they're bringing.
Who can live without it?
I ask in all honesty;
What would life be?
Without a song or a dance, what are we?
So I say thank you for the music,
For giving it to me.

Sophie:

I've been so lucky,
I am the girl with golden hair.
I wanna sing it out to everybody,
What a joy! What a life! What a chance!

Sophie/Harry/Bill/Sam:

Thank you for the music, the songs I'm singing,
Thanks for all the joy they're bringing.
Who can live without it?
I ask in all honesty,
What would life be?
Without a song or a dance, what are we?
So I say thank you for the music,
For giving it to me.

So I say thank you for the music,

Sophie:

For giving it to me.

There's Gotta Be Something Better Than This

Music by Cy Coleman
Lyrics by Dorothy Fields

from *Sweet Charity*

There's Gotta Be Something Better Than This,
There's gotta be something better to do.
And when I find me something better to do,
I'm gonna get up, I'm gonna get out,
I'm gonna get up, get out and do it!

There's gotta be some respectable trade,
There's gotta be something easy to learn.
And if I find me something a half-wit can learn,
I'm gonna get up, I'm gonna get out,
I'm gonna get up, get out and learn it!

No more griping, I have had it,
No more groaning, grumbling, wailing, sighing,
Weeping, moaning, whining, crying.

Spoken: Phooey!

There's gotta be some life cleaner than this,
There's gotta be some good reason to live.
And when I find me some kind of life I can live,
I'm gonna get up, I'm gonna get out,
I'm gonna get up, I'm gonna get out,
I'm gonna get up, I'm gonna get out,
I'm gonna get up, get out and live it!

Think Of Me

Music by Andrew Lloyd Webber
Lyrics by Charles Hart
Additional Lyrics by Richard Stilgoe

from *The Phantom Of The Opera*

Christine:
Think of me,
Think of me fondly when we've said
   goodbye.
Remember me,
Ev'ry so often, promise me you'll try.
On that day, that not so distant day,
When you are far away and free,
If you ever find a moment,
Spare a thought for me.

And though it's clear,
Though it was always clear,
That this was never meant to be,
If you happen to remember,
Stop and think of me.

Think of August,
When the trees were green.
Don't think about the way
Things might have been.

Think of me,
Think of me waking, silent and resigned.
Imagine me,
Trying too hard to put you from my mind.
Think of me, please say you'll think of me,
Whatever else you choose to do.
There will never be a day
When I won't think of you.

Raoul:
Can it be,
Can it be Christine?
Long ago,
It seems so long ago,
How young and innocent we were.
She may not remember me,
But I remember her.

Christine:
Flowers fade,
The fruits of summer fade,
They have their season, so do we.
But please promise me that sometimes,
You will think...of me!

This Is The Moment

Words by Leslie Bricusse
Music by Frank Wildhorn

from *Jekyll & Hyde*

This is the moment, this is the day,
When I send all my doubts and demons on
    their way.
Every endeavor I have made ever come in into
    play,
Is here and now today.

This is the moment, this is the time
When the momentum and the moment are in
    rhyme.
Give me this moment, this precious chance.
I'll gather up my past and make some sense at
    last.

This is the moment when all I've done,
All of the dreaming, scheming and screaming
    become one!
This is the day, see it sparkle and shine,
When all I've lived for becomes mine!

For all these years I've faced the world alone,
And now the time has come
To prove to them I made it on my own.

This is the moment, my final test.
Destiny beckoned, I never reckoned second
    best.
I won't look down, I must not fall.
This is the moment, the sweetest moment of
    them all!

This is the moment. Damn all the odds.
This day or never, I'll sit forever with the gods!
When I look back, I will always recall,
Moment for moment, this was the moment,
The greatest moment of all.

This Nearly Was Mine

Lyrics by Oscar Hammerstein II
Music by Richard Rodgers

from *South Pacific*

One dream in my heart,
One love to be living for,
One love to be living for,
This nearly was mine.

One girl for my dream,
One partner in paradise,
This promise of paradise,
This nearly was mine.

Close to my heart she came,
Only to fly away,
Only to fly as day flies from moonlight.

Now, now I'm alone
Still dreaming of paradise,
Still saying that paradise
Once nearly was mine.

So clear and deep are my fancies
Of things I wish were true,
I'll keep remembering evenings
I wish I'd spent with you.

I'll keep remembering kisses
From lips I'll never own,
And all the lovely adventures
That we have never known.

Now, now I'm alone
Still dreaming of paradise,
Still saying that paradise
Once nearly was mine.

Till There Was You

Words & Music by Meredith Willson

from *The Music Man*

There were bells
On the hill,
But I never heard them ringing.
No, I never heard them at all,
Till there was you.

There were birds
In the sky,
But I never saw them winging.
No, I never saw them at all,
Till there was you.

And there was music,
And there were wonderful roses,
They tell me,
In sweet fragrant meadows of dawn
And dew.

There was love
All around,
But I never heard it singing.
No, I never heard it at all,
Till there was you.

Tomorrow

Lyric by Martin Charnin
Music by Charles Strouse

from *Annie*

The sun'll come out tomorrow,
Bet your bottom dollar that tomorrow,
There'll be sun!
Just thinkin' about tomorrow
Clears away the cobwebs and the sorrow,
'Til there's none!

Refrain:
When I'm stuck with a day that's gray and
    lonely,
I just stick out my chin and grin and say:
Oh, the sun'll come out tomorrow,
So ya gotta hang on 'til tomorrow,
Come what may!
Tomorrow, tomorrow,
I love ya, tomorrow,
You're always a day away!

Refrain

Tomorrow, tomorrow,
I love ya, tomorrow,
You're always a day away!

Too Close For Comfort

Words & Music by Jerry Bock, Larry Holofcener & George Weiss

from *Mr. Wonderful*

The men of science are a brilliant clan.
Just think, just think,
They can tell how far it is from here to a
　star above,
And yet they cannot measure the safest
　distance
Between a woman and man in love.
Since I cannot consult a book of knowledge
That may be lying on a shelf,
I guess I'll have a confidential discussion with
　myself.

Refrain:
Be wise, be smart,
Behave my heart,
Don't upset your cart
When she's [he's] so close.
Be soft, be sweet,
But be discreet,
Don't go off your beat.
She's [He's] too close for comfort.
Too close, too close for comfort,
Please not again.
Too close, too close to know
Just when to say, "when."

Be firm, be fair,
Be sure, beware,
On your guard, take care
While there's such temptation.
One thing leads to another,
Too late to run for cover,
She's [He's] much too close for
　comfort now!

Refrain

Too close, too close.
She's [He's] much too close for comfort now.

Too Darn Hot

Words & Music by Cole Porter

from *Kiss Me, Kate*

It's too darn hot,
It's too darn hot,
I'd like to sup with my baby tonight,
And play the pup with my baby tonight.
I'd like to sup with my baby tonight,
And play the pup with my baby tonight,
But I ain't up to my baby tonight
'Cause it's too darn hot.

It's too darn hot,
It's too darn hot,
I'd like to stop for my baby tonight,
And blow my top with my baby tonight.
I'd like to stop for my baby tonight,
And blow my top with my baby tonight,
But I'd be a flop with my baby tonight
'Cause it's too darn hot.

It's too darn hot,
It's too darn hot,
I'd like to fool with my baby tonight,
Break ev'ry rule with my baby tonight.
I'd like to fool with my baby tonight,
Break ev'ry rule with my baby tonight.
But pillow, you'll be my baby tonight
'Cause it's too darn hot.

According to the Kinsey report
Ev'ry average man you know
Much prefers to play his favorite sport
When the temperature is low,
But when the thermometer goes 'way up
And the weather is sizzling hot,
Mister Adam
For his madam
Is not.
'Cause it's too, too,
Too darn hot,
It's too darn hot,
It's too darn hot.

It's too darn hot,
It's too darn hot.
I'd like to call on my baby tonight,
And give my all to my baby tonight,
I'd like to call on my baby tonight,
And give my all to my baby tonight,
But I can't play ball with my baby tonight
'Cause it's too darn hot.

It's too darn hot,
It's too darn hot.
I'd like to meet with my baby tonight,
Get off my feet with my baby tonight,
I'd like to meet with my baby tonight,
Get off my feet with my baby tonight,
But no repeat with my baby tonight,
'Cause it's too darn hot.

It's too darn hot,
It's too darn hot.
I'd like to coo to my baby tonight,
And pitch the woo with my baby tonight,
I'd like to coo to my baby tonight,
And pitch the woo with my baby tonight,
But, brother, you bite my baby tonight,
'Cause it's too darn hot.

According to the Kinsey report,
Ev'ry average man you know
Much prefers to play his favorite sport
When the temperature is low,
But when the thermometer goes 'way up
And the weather is sizzling hot,
Mister Gob
For his squab,
A marine
For his queen,
A G.I.
For his cutie pie
Is not.
'Cause it's too, too,
Too darn hot.

Two Ladies

Music by John Kander
Lyrics by Fred Ebb

from *Cabaret*

1st girl:
Beedle dee deedle dee dee!

2nd girl:
Beedle dee deedle dee dee!

M.C.:
Beedle dee, deeldle dee,
Beedle dee deedle dee dee!

Girls:
Beedle dee dee dee dee,

M.C.:
Two ladies.

Girls:
Beedle dee dee dee dee,

M.C.:
Two ladies.

Girls:
Beedle dee dee dee dee

M.C.:
And I'm the only man, ja!

Girls:
Beedle dee dee dee dee,

M.C.:
I like it.

Girls:
Beedle dee dee dee dee,

M.C.:
They like it.

Girls:
Beedle dee dee dee dee,

M.C.:
This two for one. Beedle dee dee dee dee.

Girls:
Two ladies.

M.C.:
Beedle dee dee dee dee,

Girls:
Two ladies.

M.C.:
Beedle dee dee dee dee,

Girls:
And he's the only man.

All:
Ja!

Girls:
Beedle dee dee dee dee,

Girl 1:
He likes it.

M.C.:
Beedle dee dee dee dee,

Girl 2:
We like it.

M.C.:
Beedle dee dee dee dee,

Girls:
This two for one.

Girl 1:
I do the cooking,

Girl 2:
And I make the bed.

M.C.:
I go out daily to earn our daily bread.
But we've got one thing in common
He, she and me,

Girl 1:
The key,

M.C.:
Beedle dee dee

Girl 1:
The key,

M.C.:
Beedle dee dee

Girl 1:
The key

Girls:
Beedle dee deedle dee deedle dee dee.

Girls:
Beedle dee dee dee dee,

M.C.:
Two ladies.

Girls:
Beedle dee dee dee dee,

M.C.:
Two ladies.

Girls:
Beedle dee dee dee dee

M.C.:
And I'm the only man, ja!

Girls:
Beedle dee dee dee dee,

M.C.:
I like it.

Girls:
Beedle dee dee dee dee,

M.C.:
They like it.

Girls:
Beedle dee dee dee dee,

M.C.:
This two for one. Beedle dee dee dee dee

Girls:
Two ladies.

M.C.:
Beedle dee dee dee dee,

Girls:
Two ladies.

M.C.:
Beedle dee dee dee dee,

Girls:
And he's the only man.

M.C.:
Ja!

Girls:
Beedle dee dee dee dee,

Girl 1:
He likes it

M.C.:
Beedle dee dee dee dee,

Girl 2:
We like it.

M.C.:
Beedle dee dee dee dee,

Girls:
This two for one.

M.C.:
We switch partners daily to play as we please,

Girls:
Two-sie beats one-sie, but nothing beats threes.

M.C.:
I sleep in the middle,

Girl 1:
I'm left

Girl 2:
And I'm right.

M.C.:
But there's room on the bottom if you drop in
    some night.

Girls:
Beedle dee dee dee dee.

M.C.:
Two ladies. Beedle dee dee dee dee,

Girls:
Two ladies. Beedle dee dee dee dee,
And he's the only man. Beedle dee dee dee dee,

M.C.:
I like it, Beedle dee dee dee dee
They like it!

Girls:
Beedle dee dee dee dee

All:
This two for one. Beedle dee deedle dee deedle
    dee deedle dee dee!

Unexpected Song

Music by Andrew Lloyd Webber
Lyrics by Don Black

from *Song & Dance*

I have never felt like this,
For once I'm lost for words,
Your smile has really thrown me.
This is not like me at all,
I never thought I'd know
The kind of love you've shown me.

Refrain:
Now no matter where I am,
No matter what I do,
I see your face appearing
Like an unexpected song,
An unexpected song
That only we are hearing.

I don't know what's going on,
Can't work it out at all.
Whatever made you choose me?
I just can't believe my eyes,
You look at me as though
You couldn't bear to lose me.

Refrain

I have never felt like this.
For once I'm lost for words,
Your smile has really thrown me.
This is not like me at all,
I never thought I'd know
The kind of love you've shown me.

Now no matter where I am,
No matter what I do,
I see your appearing
Like an unexpected song,
An unexpected song
That only we are hearing.
Like an unexpected song,
An unexpected song
That only we are hearing.

Unusual Way (In A Very Unusual Way)

Words & Music by Maury Yeston

from *Nine*

In a very unusual way,
One time I needed you.
In a very unusual way,
You were my friend.
Maybe it lasted a day,
Maybe it lasted an hour,
But somehow it will never end.

In a very unusual way,
I think I'm in love with you.
In a very unusual way,
I want to cry.
Something inside me goes weak,
Something inside me surrenders,
And you're the reason why,
You're the reason why.

You don't know what you do to me,
You don't have a clue.
You can't tell what it's like to be me,
Looking at you.
It scares me so that I can hardly speak.

In a very unusual way,
I owe what I am to you.
Though at times it appears I won't stay,
I never go.
Special to me in my life,
Since the first day that I met you,
How could I ever forget you,
Once you had touched my soul?
In a very unusual way,
You've made me whole.

We Go Together

Words & Music by Warren Casey and Jim Jacobs

from *Grease*

We go together,
Like ra-ma la-ma la-ma ka ding-a da ding-dong.
Remembered forever
As shoo-bop-sha-wad-da wad-da yip-pi-ty
    boom-de-boom.
Chang chang ah chan-it-ty chang-shoo bop.
That's the way it should be, wha oooh, yeah!

We're one of a kind
Like dip da dip da dip doo wop-a doo-bee doo,
Our names are signed
Boogedy boogedy boogedy boogedy shooby doo
    wop she bop.
Chang chang ah changitty chang-shoo bop,
We'll always bee-ee like one.
Wa wa wa waaah.

When we go out at night, and stars are shining
    bright
Up in the skies above.
Or at the high school dance, where you can
    find romance,
Maybe it might be love.

We're for each other
Like-a wop ba-ba lu-mop and wop bam boom.
Just like my brother
Is sha-na-na-na-na-na yip-pi-ty dip-de doom
Chang chang ah changitty-chang–shoo bop,
We'll always be together, together.

We Kiss In A Shadow

Lyrics by Oscar Hammerstein II
Music by Richard Rodgers

from *The King & I*

We kiss in a shadow,
We hide from the moon,
Our meetings are few
And over too soon.

We speak in a whisper,
Afraid to be heard,
When people are near,
We speak not a word.

Alone in our secret,
Together we sigh,
For one smiling day to be free,

To kiss in the sunlight,
And say to the sky:
Behold and believe what you see!
Behold how my lover loves me!

What I Did For Love

Music by Marvin Hamlisch
Lyric by Edward Kleban

from *A Chorus Line*

Kiss today goodbye,
The sweetness and the sorrow.
We did what we had to do,
And I can't regret
What I did for love,
What I did for love.

Look, my eyes are dry,
The gift was ours to borrow.
It's as if we always knew,
But I won't forget
What I did for love,
What I did for love.

Gone, love is never gone,
As we travel on,
Love's what we'll remember.

Kiss today goodbye
And point me toward tomorrow.
Wish me luck, the same to you.
Won't forget, can't regret
What I did for love.

What Kind Of Fool Am I?

Words & Music by Leslie Bricusse & Anthony Newley

from *Stop the World—I Want to Get Off*

Refrain:
What kind of fool am I?
Who never fell in love,
It seems that I'm the only one
That I have been thinking of.
What kind of man is this?
An empty shell,
A lovely cell in which
An empty heart must dwell.

What kind of lips are these
That lied with every kiss?
That whispered empty words of love
That left me alone like this?
Why can't I fall in love
Like any other man
And maybe then I'll know
What kind of fool I am.

What kind of clown am I?
What do I know of life?
Why can't I cast away the mask
Of play and live my life?
Why can't I fall in love
'Til I don't give a damn
And maybe then I'll know
What kind of fool I am.

What Makes Me Love Him?

Words & Music by Jerry Bock & Sheldon Harnick

from *The Apple Tree*

What makes me love him?
It's not his singing.
I've heard his singing,
It sours the milk.
And yet,
It's gotten to the point
Where I prefer that kind of milk.

What makes me love him?
It's not his learning.
He's learned so slowly,
His whole life long.
And tho'
He really knows a multitude of things,
They're mostly wrong.

He is a good man,
Yet, I would love him
If he abused me,
Or used me ill.
And tho' he's handsome,
I know inside me,
Were he a plain man,
I'd love him still.

What makes me love him?
It's quite beyond me.
It must be something
I can't define,
Unless,
It's merely that he's masculine,
And that he's mine.

What's The Use Of Wond'rin'

Lyrics by Oscar Hammerstein II
Music by Richard Rodgers

from *Carousel*

What's the use of wond'rin'
If he's good or if he's bad,
Or if you like the way he wears his hat?
Oh, what's the use of wond'rin'
If he's good or if he's bad?
He's your feller and you love him—
That's all there is to that.

Common sense may tell you
That the endin' will be sad
And now's the time to break and run away.
But what's the use of wond'rin'
If the endin' will be sad?
He's your feller and you love him—
There's nothin' more to say.

Somethin' made him the way that he is,
Whether he's false or true.
And somethin' gave him the things that are
   his—
One of those things is you.

So, when he wants your kisses
You will give them to the lad,
And anywhere he leads you you will walk.
And any time he needs you,
You'll go runnin' there like mad.
You're his girl and he's your feller—
And all the rest is talk.

Where Was I When They Passed Out The Luck?

Words & Music by Hal Hackady & Larry Grossman

from *Minnie's Boys*

Where was I when they passed out brains?
Right at the head of the line.
Where was I when they passed out talent?
Right up front getting mine.
But when it came to the line
Where they handed out luck,
Where was your smart, clever friend?
Back, showin' off my talent and brains,
To the bums linin' up at the end.

Where was I when they passed out looks?
Needless to say I was there.
Who'll deny in the charm department,
I got more than my share.
But when the time rolled around,
And they handed out luck,
Where was your good-looking clown?
Off, tryin' out my profile and charm,
On a girl in a neighboring town!

I sure got a great sense of humor,
(Spoken) A-ha-ha!
(Sung) The day they were passing the pot.
I sure got a great sense of humor.
(Spoken) A-ha-ha!
(Sung) And I need all I got!

Where was I when they passed out guts?
Mister, I opened the store!
I'm the guy who invented chutzpah,
Show me a guy who's got more!
But when they yelled,
"Get your luck, 'cause it's runnin' out fast!
Step up and get your supply!"
Me, with my brains and talent and looks,
Blew the one thing you need to get by!
Where was I?

When The Children Are Asleep

Lyrics by Oscar Hammerstein II
Music by Richard Rodgers

from *Carousel*

Mr. Snow:
I own a little house, and I sail a little boat,
And the fish I ketch I sell.
And in a manner of speakin' I'm doin'
   very well.
I love a little girl and she's in love with me.
And soon she'll be my bride.
And in a manner of speakin' I should be
   satisfied!
Carrie (Spoken):
Well, ain't you?

Mr. Snow:
If I told you my plans, and the things I intend,
It'd make ev'ry curl on yer head stand on end!

When I make enough money outa one little
   boat,
I'll put all my money in another little boat,
I'll make twic't as much outa two little boats,
And the fust thing you know, I'll have four
   little boats!

Then eight little boats, then a fleet of little
   boats!
Then a great, big fleet of great, big boats,
All ketchin' herrin, bringin' it to shore.
Sailin' out again and bringin' in more, and
   more and more
And more!

Carrie (Spoken):
Who's goin' t' eat all that herring?

Mr. Snow (Spoken):
They ain't goin' to be herring! Goin' to put them
   in cans
And call 'em sardines. Goin' to build a little
   sardine cannery—
Then a big one—then the biggest one in the
   country.
Carrie, I'm goin' t' get rich on sardines.
I mean we're goin' t'get rich—you and me, and
   all of us.

Mr. Snow (Sung):
The fust year we're married we'll hev one
   little kid,
The second year we'll go and hev another
   little kid,
You'll soon be darnin' socks fer eight
   little feet.

Carrie:
Are you buildin' up to another fleet?

Mr. Snow:
We'll build a lot more rooms,
Our dear little house'll get bigger,
Our dear little house'll get bigger!

Carrie:
And so will my figger.

Mr. Snow (Spoken):
Carrie, ken y'imagine how it'll be
When all the kids are upstairs in bed,
And you and me sit alone in the firelight?
Me in my armchair—you on my knee—
   mebbe?

Carrie (Spoken):
Mebbe.

Mr. Snow (Sung):
When the children are asleep, we'll sit and
    dream
The things that ev'ry other dad and mother
    dream.
When the children are asleep and lights are
    low,
If I still love you
The way I love you today,
You'll pardon my saying: "I told you so!"
When the children are asleep
I'll dream with you.
We'll think, what fun we hev had
And be glad that it all came true!

Carrie:
When children are awake,
Arompin' thru the rooms and runnin' on the
    stairs,
Then in a manner of speakin'
A house is really theirs.
But once they close their eyes,
And we are left alone
And free from all their fuss,
Then in a manner of speakin'
We can be really us.
When the children are asleep,
(Dream all alone.)
We'll sit and dream,
(Dreams that won't be interrupted,) The things
    that ev'ry other Dad and Mother dream
(Dreams that won't be interrupted,)

Mr. Snow:
When the children are asleep and lights are
    low.
(Lo! And behold.)

Carrie:
If I still love you
The way I love you today,
You'll pardon my saying: "I told you so!"
When the children are asleep
I'll dream with you,
(You'll dream with me.)
We'll think what fun we hev had
And be glad that it all came true.

Mr. Snow:
When today is a long time ago.

Both:
You'll still hear me say that the best dream I
    know is:

Carrie:
When the children are asleep
I'll dream with you!

Mr. Snow:
You!

Willkommen

Music by John Kander
Lyrics by Fred Ebb

from *Cabaret*

Chorus:
Willkommen! Bien-venue! Welcome!
Fremder, étranger, stranger,
Glucklich zu sehen. Je suis enchanté.
Happy to see you, Bleibe, reste, stay,
Willkommen! Bien-venue! Welcome!
Im Cabaret, au Cabaret, to Cabaret!

Spoken:
Meine damen und herren,
Messieurs et mes dames,
Ladies and gentlemen,
Guten abend, bon soir, good evening;
Wie gehts? Comment ça va? Do you feel good?
Ich bin euer confrencier
Je suis votre compère,
I am your host!

Sung:
Und sage, Willkommen! Bien-venue! Welcome!
Im Cabaret, au Cabaret, to Cabaret!

Wishing You Were Somehow Here Again

Music by Andrew Lloyd Webber
Lyrics by Charles Hart
Additional Lyrics by Richard Stilgoe

from *The Phantom Of The Opera*

You were once my one companion,
You were all that mattered.
You were once a friend and father,
Then my world was shattered.

Wishing you were somehow here again,
Wishing you were somehow near,
Sometimes it seemed
If I just dreamed,
Somehow you would be here.

Wishing I could hear your voice again,
Knowing that I never would,
Dreaming of you
Won't help me to do
All that you dreamed I could.

Passing bells and sculpted angels,
Cold and monumental,
Seem for you the wrong companions,
You were warm and gentle.

Too many years,
Fighting back tears,
Why can't the past just die?

Wishing you were somehow here again,
Knowing we must say good-bye.
Try to forgive,
Teach me to live,
Give me the strength to try.

No more memories, no more silent tears,
No more gazing across the wasted years.
Help me say good-bye!
Help me say good-bye!

The Winner Takes It All

Words & Music by Benny Andersson & Björn Ulvaeus

from *Mamma Mia!*

I don't want to talk
About things we've gone through,
Though it's hurting me
Now its history.
I've played all my cards,
And that's what you've done too.
Nothing more to say,
No more ace to play.

The winner takes it all
The loser standing small
Beside the victory
That's her destiny

I was in your arms
Thinking I belonged there.
I figured it made sense,
Building me a fence.
Building me a home.
Thinking I'd be strong there.
But I was a fool,
Playing by the rules.

The gods may throw the dice
Their minds as cold as ice.
And someone way down here
Loses someone dear.
The winner takes it all
The loser has to fall
Its simple and its plain
Why should I complain?

But tell me does she kiss
Like I used to kiss you?
Does it feel the same
When she calls your name?

Somewhere deep inside
You must know I miss you
But what can I say?
Rules must be obeyed.

The judges will decide.
The likes of me abide.
Spectators of the show
Always staying low.

The game is one again
A lover or a friend
A big thing or a small
The winner takes it all.

I don't wanna talk
'cause it makes me feel sad.
And I understand
You've come to shake my hand.

I apologise
If it makes you feel bad
Seeing me so tense
No self-confidence.

But you see
The winner takes it all.
The winner takes it all.

The game is on again
A lover or a friend
A big thing or a small
The winner takes it all.

The winner takes it all.

With One Look

Music by Andrew Lloyd Webber
Lyrics by Don Black and Christopher Hampton,
With contributions by Amy Powers

from *Sunset Boulevard*

With one look I can break your heart,
With one look I play every part.
I can make your sad heart sing,
With one look you'll know all you need to
    know.

With one smile I'm the girl next door
Or the love that you've hungered for.
When I speak it's with my soul
I can play any role.

No words can tell the stories my eyes tell,
Watch me when I frown, you can't write
    that down.
You know I'm right, it's there in black
    and white,
When I look your way you'll hear what I say.

Yes, with one look I put words to shame,
Just one look sets the screen aflame.
Silent music starts to play,
One tear in my eye makes the whole
    world cry.

With one look they'll forgive the past,
They'll rejoice I've returned at last
To my people in the dark,
Still out there in the dark.

Silent music starts to play.
With one look you'll know all you need
    to know.
With one look I'll ignite a blaze,
I'll return to my glory days.

They'll say Norma's back at last.
This time I'm staying for good,
I'll be back where I was born to be,
With one look I'll be me.

A Woman In Love

Words & Music by Frank Loesser

from *Guys & Dolls*

Sky & Sarah:
Your eyes are the eyes of a woman in love
And oh, how they give you away.
Why try to deny you're a woman in love,
When I know very well what I say.
I say no moon in the sky ever lent such a glow,
Some flame deep within made them shine.
Those eyes are the eyes of a woman in love
And may they gaze evermore into mine,
Crazily gaze evermore into mine.

(Repeat)

A Wonderful Guy

Lyrics by Oscar Hammerstein II
Music by Richard Rodgers

from *South Pacific*

I expect every one
Of my crowd to make fun
Of my proud protestations of faith in romance,
And they'll say I'm naïve
As a babe to believe
Any fable I hear from a person in pants.

Fearlessly I'll face them and argue their doubts
   away.
Loudly I'll sing about flowers and spring.
Flatly I'll stand on my little flat feet and say,
Love is a grand and a beautiful thing!
I'm not ashamed to reveal
The world-famous feeling I feel.

I'm as corny as Kansas in August,
I'm as normal as blueberry pie.
No more a smart
Little girl with no heart,
I have found me a wonderful guy.
I am in a conventional dither
With a conventional star in my eye,
And you will note
There's a lump in my throat
When I speak of that wonderful guy.

I'm as trite and as gay
As a daisy in May,
A cliché coming true!
I'm bromidic and bright
As a moon-happy night
Pouring light on the dew.
I'm as corny as Kansas in August,
High as a flag on the Fourth of July!
If you'll excuse
An expression I use,
I'm in love,
I'm in love,
I'm in love,
I'm in love,
I'm in love with a wonderful guy!

Wouldn't It Be Loverly

Words by Alan Jay Lerner
Music by Frederick Loewe

from *My Fair Lady*

All I want is a room somewhere,
Far away from the cold night air,
With one enormous chair,
Oh, wouldn't it be loverly?

Lots of choc'late for me to eat,
Lots of coal makin' lots of heat,
Warm face, warm hands, warm feet,
Oh, wouldn't it be loverly?

Oh, so loverly sittin'
Abso-bloomin'-lutely still!
I would never budge 'til
Spring crept over me windersill.

Someone's head restin' on my knee,
Warm and tender as he can be,
Who takes good care of me,
Oh, wouldn't it be loverly?
Loverly!

Written In The Stars

Music by Elton John
Lyrics by Tim Rice

from Walt Disney Theatrical Production *Aida*

Male:
I am here to tell you we can never
  meet again.
Simple really, isn't it?
A word or two and then a lifetime of
  not knowing
Where or why or when.
You think of me or speak of me
Or wonder what befell
The someone you once loved
So long ago so well.

Female:
Never wonder what I'll feel as
  living shuffles by.
You don't have to ask me and
  I need not reply.
Every moment of my life from now until I die
I will think or dream of you and fail to
  understand
How a perfect love can be confounded
  out of hand.

Both:
Is it written in the stars?
Are we paying for some crime?
Is that all that we are good for,
Just a stretch of mortal time?
Is this God's experiment in which
  we have no say?
In which we're given paradise,
  but only for a day.

Male:
Nothing can be altered.
  Oh, there is nothing to decide.
No escape, no change of heart nor
  any place to hide.

Female:
You are all I'll ever want but this
  I am denied.
Sometimes in my darkest thoughts
I wish I never learned what it is
To be in love and have that love returned.

Both:
Is it written in the stars?
Are we paying for some crime?
Is that all that we are good for,
Just a stretch of mortal time?
Is this God's experiment in which
  we have no say?
In which we're given paradise,
  but only for a day.
Is it written in the stars?
Are we paying for some crime?
Is that all that we are good for,
Just a stretch of mortal time?

Male:
In which we have no say?

Female:
In which we're given paradise only

Both:
For a day.

You And I

Words & Music by Benny Andersson, Tim Rice & Björn Ulvaeus
from *Chess*

The Russian:
Knowing I want you, Knowing I love you
I can't explain why I remain careless about you.

Florence:
I've been a fool to allow dreams to become
    great expectations.

The Russian:
How can I love you so much yet make no move?

Both:
I pray the days and nights in their endless
    weary procession
Soon overwhelm my sad obsession.
You and I we've seen it all chasing our heart's
    desire,
But we go on pretending stories like ours have
    happy endings.

The Russian:
You could not give me more than you gave me.
Why should there be something in me still
    discontented?

Florence:
I won't look back anymore and if I do,
Just for a moment,

The Russian:
I'll soon be happy to say I knew her when.

Both:
But if you hear today
I'm no longer quite so devoted to this affair,
I've been misquoted.

You and I we've seen it all chasing our heart's
    desire,
But we go on pretending stories like ours have
    happy endings.

You Are Beautiful

Lyrics by Oscar Hammerstein II
Music by Richard Rodgers

from *Flower Drum Song*

You are beautiful,
Small and shy,
You are the girl whose eyes met mine
Just as your boat sailed by.

This I know of you,
Nothing more:
You are the girl whose eyes met mine,
Passing the river shore.

You are the girl whose laugh I heard,
Silver and soft and bright;
Soft as the fall of lotus leaves
Brushing the air of night.

While your flower boat
Sailed away,
Gently your eyes looked back on mine,
Clearly you heard me say:
"You are the girl I will love someday."

You Must Love Me

Music by Andrew Lloyd Webber
Lyrics by Tim Rice

from *Evita*

Where do we go from here?
This isn't where we intended to be.
We had it all, you believed in me,
I believed in you.
Certainties disappear,
What do we do for our dream to survive,
How do we keep all our passions alive
As we used to do?

Deep in my heart I'm concealing
Things that I'm longing to say,
Scared to confess what I'm feeling,
Frightened you'll slip away,
You must love me,
You must love me.

Oo…
Why are you at my side?
How can I be any use to you now?
Give me a chance and I'll let you see how
Nothing has changed.
Deep in my heart I'm concealing
Things that I'm longing to say,
Scared to confess what I'm feeling,

You'll Never Walk Alone

Lyrics by Oscar Hammerstein II
Music by Richard Rodgers

from *Carousel*

When you walk through a storm, hold your
    head up high
And don't be afraid of the dark,
At the end of the storm is a golden sky
And the sweet silver song of a lark.

Walk on through the wind,
Walk on through the wind,
Walk on through the rain,
Tho' your dreams be tossed and blown,
Walk on, walk on, with hope in your heart,
And you'll never walk alone,
You'll never walk alone!

You're The One That I Want

Words & Music by John Farrar

from *Grease*

I got chills. They're multiplyin' and I'm losin'
  control.
`Cause the power you're supplyin', (it's
  electrifyin'!)
Feel your way. You better shape up,
Cause I need a man and my heart is set on
  you.
You better shape up; you better understand
To my heart I must be true.
(Nothin' left, nothin' left for me to do.)

You're the one that I want.
You, oo, oo, honey, the one that I want
You, oo, oo, honey, the one that I want
You, oo, oo, are what I need, oh yes indeed.

If you're filled with affection you're too shy to
  convey,
Meditate in my direction. (It's electrifyin'!)
Feel your way. I better shape up,
`Cause you need a man who can keep you
  satisfied.
I better shape up if I'm gonna prove
That your faith is justified.
(Are you sure? Yes I'm sure down deep
  inside.)

You're the one that I want.
You, oo, oo, honey, the one that I want
You, oo, oo, honey, the one that I want
You, oo, oo, are what I need, oh yes indeed.

You're the one that I want.
You, oo, oo, honey, the one that I want
You, oo, oo, honey, the one that I want.

You've Got To Be Carefully Taught

Lyrics by Oscar Hammerstein II
Music by Richard Rodgers

from *South Pacific*

You've got to be carefully taught to hate and
   fear.
You've got to be taught from year to year.
It's got to be drummed in your dear little ear.
You've got to be carefully taught.

You've got to be taught to be afraid
Of people whose eyes are oddly made,
And people whose skin is a different shade,
You've got to be carefully taught.

You've got to be taught before it's too late,
Before you are six, or seven, or eight,
To hate all the people your relatives hate,
You've got to be carefully taught!
You've got to be carefully taught!

Younger Than Springtime

Lyrics by Oscar Hammerstein II
Music by Richard Rodgers

from *South Pacific*

I touch your hand,
And my arms grow strong,
Like a pair of birds
That burst with song.
My eyes look down
At your lovely face,
And I hold the world
In my embrace.

Younger than springtime are you,
Softer than starlight are you,
Warmer than winds of June
Are the gentle lips you gave me.
Gayer than laughter are you,
Sweeter than music are you.
Angel and lover, heaven and earth,
Are you to me.
And when your youth and joy invade my arms
And fill my heart, as now they do,
Then, younger than springtime am I,
Gayer than laughter am I,
Angel and lover, heaven and earth,
Am I with you.

Show Index

Show Index

Songwriter
Index

Songwriter Index